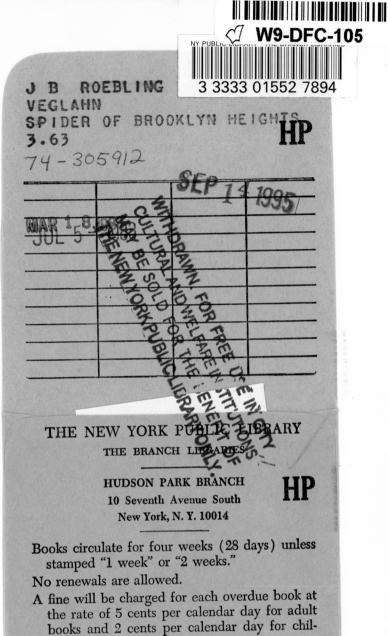

the spider of brooklyn heights

NANCY VEGLAHN

the spider of brooklyn heights

CHARLES SCRIBNER'S SONS   NEW YORK

I am grateful to Doris Phillips and Caroline McGibney of the Black Hills State College Library for help in obtaining research materials and to Ray Fraley of Brady Engineering for technical advice.

For Dan, who likes to build

contents

illustrations

author's note

This is the story of Washington Augustus Roebling and his struggle to build the Brooklyn Bridge. The characters were all real people. Except for a few minor incidents, the events in the book are based on material in Washington Roebling's letters and journals and on other contemporary writings. Conversations have been invented for dramatic effect.

Washington Roebling lived for more than forty years after the completion of the Brooklyn Bridge, but he never regained his health and was unable to return to the active practice of his engineering profession. In 1888 he and Emily moved to Trenton, New Jersey. He read widely and continued his interest in collecting minerals. Fifteen thousand rare mineral specimens which he gathered are now owned by the Smithsonian Institution.

John A. Roebling II followed the family engineering tradition. He was graduated from Rensselaer in 1888. Emily Roebling died on February 28, 1903. Five years later Washington married Mrs. Cornelia Witsell Farrow of Charleston, South Carolina.

Washington Roebling died at his home in Trenton on July 21, 1926, at the age of eighty-nine. The firm of John A. Roebling's Sons is still active in Trenton, and to modern engineers the word "Roebling" is synonymous with wire rope.

1   the grand turk

Niagara Falls was as spectacular as Washington Roebling had always heard it was, and yet he could not look away from the bridge. It crossed the gorge high above the turbulent river, within sight of the falls, its mathematical precision in odd contrast with the wildness of the setting. The Grand Turk, his father's masterpiece!

"Well, what do you think of it?" Charles Swan moved closer to Washington and put a hand on his shoulder.

"It's—I just never realized it would be so big!"

"Big enough to carry a 350-ton freight train and a full load of carriages and wagons at the same time, your father says." Swan had to shout to make his soft voice carry above the roar of the falls. John Roebling's chief assistant was a slight, stooped man, whose appearance had changed little in the years Washington had known him. But today he seemed unnaturally excited, almost as proud of the bridge as if he had built it himself.

It was July, 1854, and the Grand Turk Suspension Bridge was nearly finished. Workmen bustled around Washington Roebling and Charles Swan where they stood near the approach to the bridge on the American side of the river. There were steam engines and derricks being repaired, planks being loaded and unloaded, cement and mortar being mixed, the sounds of hammers, saws, and crowbars, the shouts of foremen and workers.

For the first time Washington realized that building a bridge meant much more than drawing the neat, exacting plans he had seen in his father's study. Bringing order out of this chaos and somehow using all these materials, men, and equipment to realize the plans in stone and iron and wire: this was the task of the builder.

"Swan! What are you doing here?"

Washington recognized his father's voice and knew from its harsh tone that he was not pleased. The Chief Engineer of the Grand Turk Bridge was striding toward them through the clutter. John Roebling's dark brows were drawn together, and his mouth was a firm line above his carefully trimmed beard.

"Well?" he asked impatiently, towering above Charles Swan. "Why aren't you back in Trenton? Who's supervising the factory? And why bring the boy along?"

Swan stood his ground a little more firmly than he usually did when John Roebling confronted him. "There were some questions we needed to ask about your last specifications for wire."

"Couldn't that be done by letter?"

"You said you needed it right away, and we weren't sure. . . . I'll go back on Sunday, so I'll only miss two days of work. Werner and the others can handle things until then; it's only routine." Swan hesitated, then went on. "At any rate, I've been wanting to bring Washington up here to see the bridge before it's finished. He'll be going off to Rensselaer next fall, and I thought it might help him in his engineering studies if he could get a look at the Grand Turk under construction.

John Roebling glanced at Washington and seemed to relax a little. "Well, I suppose that part's all right, though I'm not sure how much a sixteen-year-old boy can learn in a day or two up here. . . ."

"I'm seventeen, Father." Washington disliked the way they were talking about him as though he weren't there.

"Seventeen? Yes, I suppose so," John said vaguely. "As long as you're here, I may as well show you around."

For the next three hours Washington listened, fascinated, as his father explained each step in the building of the great bridge. He told how they had built the four brick towers, each sixty feet high. Then there were the two anchorages to which the cables were bound, cast-iron plates imbedded in concrete and masonry. Finally, he spoke of the cables themselves, and as he talked, Washington studied the shining strands of wire that went over the tops of the towers and then arched out above the river. He knew this was his father's most important invention, rope made of iron wire. He knew how strong it was, how carefully it had been tested in the Trenton factory. Yet, against the backdrop of the falls, the rocky gorge, and boiling river, the wire cables seemed as slender as the strings of the violin he played in the family musicales at home.

"And what about the roadway?" Washington asked when his father paused.

"Oh, we're building that now. It's to be double-decked—the road below and the train tracks above. It's simple enough to put up a roadway. The real work is done here. Towers, anchorages, cables—those are the main parts of a suspension bridge. Remember that. If you build those three parts well, your roadway is a minor problem."

"But will it really be strong enough to carry trains?" Seeing his father's face darken, Washington hastily went on. "I mean, I'm sure it will, but I've heard some people back in Trenton say that suspension bridges aren't equipped to carry railroad trains." Washington mentioned the furor a month earlier when the suspension bridge built by Charles Ellett at Wheeling, West Virginia, had blown down. "Ellett's bridge was touted as one of the engineering marvels of the age, but the first bad storm tore it to bits."

3

"Of course Ellett's bridge couldn't hold up," said John Roebling. "He didn't make it stiff enough. That's the secret in building a suspension bridge. You have to hold the roadway so firmly that storms or traffic can't start it vibrating. Ellett tried to depend on his cables to carry the whole load." Roebling pointed out the diagonal lines of wire splayed out from the towers to the roadways. "I've used all these additional trusses to hold the road steady. I may even decide to add more beneath the bridge."

"But trains are so heavy. . . ."

John cut him off brusquely. "That's not important. We can always make the cables heavier and stronger to hold extra weight. It isn't weight that makes bridges collapse, it's vibrations. A train isn't half as hard on a bridge as a herd of cattle trotting across, a troop of soldiers marching in step, or a shifting wind. My bridge can take anything. Let's go across, and I'll show you."

They walked out on the unfinished lower deck of the bridge, stepping around the workmen who were busy laying the roadway. As they neared the center of the span, where the four main cables nearly reached the roadway of the deck above them, Washington saw that they were not nearly as slender as they looked from the shore—in fact, they were bigger around than his fist. His father had told him that there were exactly 3,640 wires in each of the main cables. The breeze from the falls was exhilarating and so was the view. But the bridge stood as firm as bedrock beneath their feet.

"How is your mother?" asked the engineer.

"Oh, she's all right, I guess," said Washington. "She's just tired all the time. It's too much for her—taking care of all of us in that little house. Do you realize there are twenty-six people living there now? Nine of us, seven of the Meissners, and ten workmen from the plant. There's even someone sleeping in the bathroom!"

"I intend to build a new house for the family as soon as I get this bridge finished," said John Roebling. "Your sisters are old enough to be of some help; there's your Aunt Amalia Meissner."

"Yes, that's true, but Edmund's been sick lately. . . ."

"Edmund? Who is Edmund?"

"Edmund Roebling, your youngest son . . . Father!" Washington was frightened by the harshness with which he spoke. He had never dared to talk that way to his father before. He turned and hurried back toward shore, wanting to end the discussion before he said something even worse.

Stumbling along the unfinished bridge, he remembered the last Christmas. His father had not been there, as usual; the Grand Turk was too important to be left even for a few days. Johanna Roebling had tried to conceal her disappointment from the children. Yet they knew that she had counted on his being home this year. Not even a letter had come—only those postscripts at the bottom of business letters to Charles Swan: "Please read this to Mrs. Roebling. It will save me writing her."

A week after Christmas Edmund had been born. And then there had been another note on a letter to Swan. Washington had seen the letter in the office where he helped after school, and each word was engraved on his memory:

Your letters of the 2nd and 3rd came to hand. You say in your last, that Mrs. Roebling and the child are pretty well. This takes me by surprise not having been informed at all of the delivery of Mrs. R. Or what do you mean?

He had not even known of the birth of his son until a week after it had taken place, and then only from a business letter from his foreman! That was typical of John Roebling, the master builder who hardly knew he had a family except for those rare visits which he used to enforce strict German discipline on the children. Washington's most vivid memories of his father had to do with angry scoldings and birch rods.

He found a place on shore where he could be alone, a little way downstream from the bustling work yard, and looked back at the bridge. How odd, he thought, that such a man could build a thing so beautiful. It seemed as though all that was good and useful in him was poured into his bridges. And this one above all others claimed his total attention: the Grand Turk, the first railway suspension bridge in the world. John Roebling had been here for most of the past four years, unwilling to turn over any part of the work to his assistants.

"Washington?" Roebling's voice sounded strangely tentative as he approached his son. "I—I know I've neglected you and your mother and the other children. Try to understand. I have to be here, to follow every step of the building, check the materials, solve the problems."

"You drew the plans. Can't someone else follow your instructions, at least part of the time?" Washington, although surprised at his father's unexpected admission of guilt, was not willing to give up easily.

"No. This is my creation, and I have to *see* that it's done right. A good bridge cannot be built by correspondence. It's a responsibility. Think of the Wheeling bridge, Washington. What if there had been people on it when it collapsed? There will be trains running over my bridge every day, and it must hold up."

"I suppose so. But when this is finished, will you spend some time at home?"

"I promise you I'll build that new house for your mother next spring, as soon as I'm done here. Of course, I'll have to get back to work after that. There's talk of a bridge over the Ohio River and another over the Allegheny at Pittsburgh. I even have an idea for bridging the East River to link New York and Brooklyn. You'll be at Rensselaer next fall, and in a few years you'll be an engineer. I'd hoped you might work with me on some of these projects."

Washington had never heard his father address him as an adult, almost an equal. He was so amazed that he did not know how to answer. But the idea of helping to plan and build one of these great suspension bridges excited him. It had always been assumed that he would be an engineer. Now he began to believe it himself, to live it in his imagination.

They had been walking back toward the anchorage as they talked. Where the cables passed into the masonry, hung a "buggy," a bucket-like seat used by the workmen in wrapping and painting the cables. John Roebling touched it and looked at Washington. "You can't really get the feel of the bridge just by walking on it," he said. "You ought to ride up to the top of one of the towers, sit up there by the saddle. Here, climb in, and we'll hoist you up."

Almost before he realized what was happening, Washington was sitting in the buggy. His father started the small engine that ran the traveling rope to the top of the tower and back. The chair swayed wildly, and for a moment he was sure he would be dumped to the ground far below. Then it clanked to a stop, and he climbed out.

The top of the tower was at least eight feet square and perfectly solid, with tons of masonry supporting it from below. Yet Washington had to stay on his knees at first, holding tightly to the traveling rope. In the middle of the tower was the "saddle," over which passed two of the main cables. There were no hand-rails, nothing between him and open space. What had seemed a slight breeze on the ground struck him like a gale that would sweep him off the tower.

Then he looked up. He could see for miles. Even the falls were dwarfed by the panorama of trees and road, villages and lakes and farms. He got to his feet and stood firmly, feeling the heat of the sun, yet cooled by the misty wind. The dizziness passed, and he dared to look below at the tiny workmen and toy machines and the Niagara River three hundred feet down. And there was the bridge, stretched across the gorge and framed by the web of steel wires supporting it.

He was part of the bridge. For that moment he was one with the steel and concrete, bricks and planks that made up the Grand Turk. He could almost understand why his father had to be here no matter how he was needed at home. To have created such a thing and watched it grow and take shape—what an experience that must have been!

Washington glanced below and saw his father waving to him, gesturing toward the buggy. He climbed in, and a few seconds later he was back on the ground.

"You got your legs in a hurry," said John Roebling. "Most of the men have to be up there longer than that before they dare to stand up straight. But it's quite a sight, isn't it?"

Washington nodded. "And the bridge is the most beautiful part of it."

John Roebling looked pleased and proud, an expression his son had not often seen. "It is beautiful, now that it's almost finished. At first a bridge is only a mass of details, a plan, and a lot of problems. But I can see the end now. And it's a good bridge. It will last."

Washington could not resist asking the question that had been bothering him, even at the risk of angering his father again. "But how do you *know?* No one's ever built a successful railroad suspension bridge before. How can you be so sure the Grand Turk won't blow down like the Wheeling bridge?"

"I told you, it's a matter of stiffening," John Roebling said impatiently. "Figuring the strength of a bridge is simple; you'll learn how to do it at Rensselaer. A train weighing 245 tons and

8

"The Grand Turk," John Roebling's suspension bridge at Niagara Falls. This daguerrotype was taken by an unknown photographer in 1855 or somewhat later.

going twenty miles an hour has a vertical impact of four hundred tons. Then you add the weight of several teams of horses and a foot of snow. Figure that and multiply it by five, the safety factor. That's the weight the cables will have to hold. Then you have to use good wire. I solved that by manufacturing my own."

It all sounded very logical, and the bridge certainly seemed solid. Yet Washington could not help thinking that Charles Ellett must have considered his bridge strong enough, too. Several other, smaller suspension bridges had also collapsed in recent years. But not, he reminded himself, one of his father's bridges. The Roebling bridges on the Pennsylvania Canal, the suspension aqueduct, and the bridge over the Monongahela all stood as firm as when they had been built.

Charles Swan had been talking with one of the foremen nearby, and now they joined the Roeblings. "I think I understand the wire specifications you sent," said Swan. "George, here, explained it to me."

"Which he might just as easily have done by mail," John Roebling reminded him. "You'll take the next train back—when does it leave?" There was no sign of the temporary thaw during which he had revealed something of himself to his son.

"We can go at nine tonight or tomorrow at eleven."

"Go tonight; then you can get in some hours at the factory tomorrow. Now come into the office for a moment; I want to mark down the expenses for this trip."

"Since I didn't come under your orders," said Swan hesitantly, "I had thought to pay for the tickets myself."

"It's business, however mistaken you were in coming here. And you brought my son along."

Washington wanted to see the office, so he followed them in. The little shack was cluttered and hot. It was obvious that the Chief Engineer did little work here; he must be on the site most of the time.

John Roebling wrote down the exact cost of the train fare, the lunches they had had on the way, even the hack Swan had hired to drive them to the station. He counted out the money and handed it to Swan. Then he took a notebook out of his desk drawer. Washington recognized it at once. It was an account book his father kept on each of the children. Washington was the oldest, so his section in the notebook was longest. Any excursion on which he had been taken, everything he had ever been given, each piece of clothing, each book was listed there.

It made him feel like one of his father's machines. John Roebling found a fresh page and recorded the sum carefully.

As they left the office, there was a commotion among the workers on the bridge approach. The foreman came running and reported breathlessly:

"It's Kurt Meier! He collapsed! I don't know what's wrong."

"I'll have a look," said John Roebling. They hurried to the group gathered around the fallen workman. The Chief Engineer shouldered his way through the crowd and knelt beside the sick man.

The man was doubled up and moaning with pain. His face was pale and greenish, and he clutched at his stomach. "It looks as if . . ." John Roebling began and then stopped. "It looks as if he might have food poisoning. A couple of you get him to bed and call a doctor."

When the man had been carried away, Roebling took his son and Charles Swan aside. "Get down to the railroad station. *Now.* And don't talk to anyone on the way. You can wait there for the train."

"What is it?" asked Washington.

"I'm not sure, but I'm afraid it's cholera. If it is, that man'll be dead by nightfall. And everyone else in the area will be in danger. I don't want you taking it back to Trenton."

"If it does turn out to be the cholera, hadn't you better get away from here?" asked Swan.

"Leave the bridge? Of course not. This is one of the most critical times. The finishing work has to be done perfectly."

"Close down until the epidemic passes."

"Impossible. I have a deadline to meet. Anyway, it's too late to stop the disease now, no matter what we do. So we may as well be working."

"But you might at least remove yourself, come back to

Trenton for a while. They could hardly finish the bridge if the Chief Engineer died of cholera," said Washington.

"And if I ran away, do you think the men would go on working?" John Roebling asked. "An engineer has to be willing to take the same risks as his workers. If there's a cholera outbreak here, I'll take my chances with the others. And you don't need to worry: I won't get it."

Seeing the firm line of his father's jaw and the determined set of his shoulders, Washington knew that John Roebling had made up his mind not to come down with cholera. And he had no doubt that his father's will was stronger than the most deadly disease.

He turned and followed Charles Swan to the railroad station.

2 allegheny

"It's working fine now, Mr. Roebling."

Washington stood up and stretched his aching muscles, as the workmen resumed drawing wire on the rope-walk at the factory. It was the third time he had had to repair the machine that week; he would write Father that it must be replaced.

It was almost a year since Washington had taken off his green uniform and come home from Rensselaer Polytechnic Institute, a graduate civil engineer. And here he was, still supervising the manufacture of wire rope in Trenton. He thought bitterly of his father's words that day at Niagara: "I'd hoped you might work with me some day."

Washington remembered his excitement on the ride back from Niagara at the prospect of working with his father on the next big bridge. There had been anxiety, too, with the news of the cholera epidemic. His father had not come down with it, of course. But more than sixty people had died in the first week, and work on the bridge had come to a standstill. John Roebling was constantly exposed to the disease, and he wrote to Swan that he had walked the floor all one night fighting cholera with sheer will power.

Finally, in the spring of Washington's first year at Rensselaer, the Niagara bridge had been opened. A train with a twenty-eight ton engine and twenty double cars was the first to cross, and the bridge held without a quiver. The news made Washington even more anxious to finish his studies. He had worked like a demon in the following months.

Three years at Rensselaer, to prepare for a job as a common mechanic! Those engineering studies had been the hardest work he had ever done. He remembered some of the courses he had had to master: Analytical Geometry of Three Dimensions, Differential and Integral Calculus, Determinative Mineralogy, Stereotomy, Acoustics, Hydraulic Motors, Kinematics, Stability of Structures. Sixty-five had entered with his class; only twelve had been graduated. And here he was, going through the same monotonous routine day after day, not even using most of that hard-earned knowledge. For he had been put in charge of the factory and Charles Swan freed to work with John Roebling at the site of the Allegheny bridge at Pittsburgh.

"The wire's beginning to look a bit more brittle than it should," Washington told his foreman as they examined the finished coils. "We'd better check the supplies of pig iron coming in. Now that we have some big orders to fill, we can't have delays because of faulty wire."

Washington and his assistant moved on to watch the application of the oil coating to the wire. The factory was working at full capacity now, to meet orders for cables, tow ropes, ropes for derricks and dredges. The business had come a long way since John Roebling had begun manufacturing the first wire rope in America in 1841.

Walking home from the factory that night, Washington felt much older than his twenty years. He was always so tired at the end of the day, and the days were so long!

A carriage was parked in front of the three-story red brick house that John Roebling had built for the family three years before. This was unusual; they rarely had guests at this time of the evening. Then Washington saw the luggage in the back and recognized the carriage as one of those that could be hired at the train station. Father had come home!

The whole family was gathered around him in the parlor, and most of the boarders as well. Johanna Roebling sat beside her husband, her glowing cheeks, her smile making her look ten years younger. Ferdinand, Laura, and Elvira were answering their father's questions shyly, while the three little boys peeked at the bearded stranger from behind their mother's skirts.

When Washington came in, the others naturally made way for him, the eldest. His father spoke with typical directness.

"Washington, I've come to take you back to Pittsburgh with me. We'll leave in the morning. It's time you did some engineering if that's what you want to be."

Past time, Washington wanted to say; I've wasted a year already. But he knew better than to speak up and perhaps spoil his chances of getting to the bridge.

"Yes, sir," he said. "And the factory . . . ?"

"Swan can handle things here."

Washington's expression must have betrayed him, for his father studied him shrewdly and said: "I suppose you think Swan could have been here all along, instead of you. You're right. But I wanted you to learn about wire, how it's made, how to judge the quality and strength. You'll need to know those things some day, believe me."

The children swarmed around Washington, congratulating him and bemoaning his departure at the same time. Ferdie, who would be going off to school himself the next year, was good-naturedly envious. The girls thought only of how they would miss their big brother. Nine-year-old Charles demanded to go along. Little Edmund and Willie were not sure what was going on, fell over each other, and began to cry.

The uproar continued through supper and long after. Johanna helped him pack his things, and though she said little

Washington guessed what she was thinking. Now the bridge was taking another of her family.

Later that evening Washington found his father working in the study on his seemingly endless philosophical manuscript entitled "Roebling's Theory of the Universe."

"How is the writing going?" Washington asked, more out of courtesy than interest. The manuscript had been in progress as long as he could remember, and the few parts he had read had seemed unbearably dull to him.

"Quite well." John Roebling put down his pen. "I'm working on the harmony of nature."

"That reminds me," said Washington, "I've been meaning to ask whether you've read anything about Dalton's theory of chemistry. We studied it my last year at Rensselaer, and I thought then that it would fit in with your idea that all nature is in harmony. If everything is made of tiny atoms, all interacting . . ."

"Atoms! Bah!" Washington's father dismissed the idea with a wave of his hand. "Who could believe in particles so small nobody can see them?"

"But Dalton presents all kinds of evidence. . . ."

"Ridiculous! Impossible!"

Washington gave up the argument, knowing from experience that it was useless to continue. John Roebling seemed to believe that he had learned everything worth knowing when he had studied with the great philosopher Hegel in Germany. It was odd that he was quite willing to profit from scientific advancements when they had to do with the practical aspects of bridge building, but he would not hear of a new theory of the world, morality, or theoretical science.

Lying in bed that night, Washington tried to decide whether Hegel's influence on his father had been good or bad. He remembered when he had been a small boy in Saxonburg, the rural community in western Pennsylvania which his father had helped to found. In those days philosophy had been a great joy to John Roebling. It played an important role in his hopes for America and influenced his plans for building beautiful structures to complement the beauty of nature. Too young to understand the words and ideas of Hegel, Washington had sensed that his father possessed an optimistic, driving faith which his teacher had instilled in him.

But since the move to Trenton things had changed. John Roebling was still interested in philosophy and still worked on his manuscript, but his single-minded devotion to bridge building seemed to drain him of intellectual energy. His ideas became fixed, and he argued vociferously with anyone who disagreed.

Washington drifted off to sleep without solving the riddle of his father's personality—or his own feelings about his father.

On the long train ride across Pennsylvania they talked about the Allegheny bridge. It was mostly on paper now, and John Roebling showed Washington the detailed plans. The spring floods had held up construction of the foundations, and they were just about ready to build the three granite piers.

The Roeblings had rooms at the "Monongahela House," but Washington saw little of them in the weeks ahead. He was at the bridge site through all hours of the day helping with the paper work and also doing physical labor.

He stood up to his knees in the still icy water of the Allegheny, directing the location of great timber piles that were driven into the river bottom where one of the piers was to be. When the piles had been driven in close together to form a watertight box, or "cofferdam," the water was pumped out of the area and workmen could begin laying the foundation of the pier.

Surprisingly, his father left him mostly to himself after the first few days. Washington began to feel more confident of his engineering skill, seeing that his father trusted his judgment.

Most of all, he enjoyed the combination of physical and

mental labor that was required of him. The hours spent poring over plans and calculations passed quickly, but that part of his responsibilities was still work. When he could use his muscles and feel the structure under his hands and feet—that was close to pure pleasure.

It was more than a year before the three piers were completed and the cast-iron towers erected on them. Finally in July, 1859, they were ready to begin spinning the cables.

Washington watched with his father as the wheel of cable wire made its first trip across the river. It swung out over the traveling rope in a smooth arc, over the tops of the towers, and reached the other side.

"Let's see," said Washington, "it will take more than four thousand trips to spin the two main cables. When do you think they'll be done?"

"Three or four months, probably, and then they'll have to be wrapped and the outside cables spun. We'll be doing well to finish the bridge by early summer."

That evening, as they were about to leave the construction site, Washington noticed a crudely lettered paper tacked to the outside gate. He moved close and squinted to read it in the fading light:

CITIZENS OF PITTSBURGH PROTEST THIS UNSAFE, FLIMSY, SO-CALLED "BRIDGE," THE GREAT UNFINISHED.

WILL IT EVER BE FINISHED? IF IT IS FINISHED, WILL WE HAVE TO PAY TOLLS TO RISK OUR LIVES ON IT? WHERE ARE THE FUNDS GOING? INTO THE POCKET OF THE FOREIGNER WHO IS BEHIND IT?"

" 'Foreigner!' " Washington repeated. "Who are they talking about?"

John Roebling said calmly, "They're talking about me. The

Know-Nothings are behind this. To them, I'm a foreigner—born and raised in Germany."

"But you've been here for more than twenty-five years!"

"Yes, and a citizen for twenty years. That makes no difference to them. I have an accent. I'm foreign-born. I'm not a real American."

"Those Know-Nothings and their so-called 'American Party.' What gives them the right to . . ." Washington stopped in mid-sentence, staring at a pile of lumber where he thought he had noticed a movement. There was a moment of silence, and then the sound of a thud, as though someone had tripped in the dark. Washington dashed across the work yard and leaped on the back of a man who was trying to scramble to his feet.

The man was small but wiry, and it took Washington a few minutes to pin him down.

"Who are you?" he asked, holding the struggling little man by both arms. There was no answer but the man's hard breathing. "Did you tack that—that thing on the gate? Are you a member of the American Party?"

"I don't know nothing about it!" the man replied shrilly.

"Let him go," said John Roebling. "He's a Know-Nothing, all right. That's what they're supposed to say when anyone asks them about the party."

"Then why let him go?"

"There's no law against putting up a sign." Reluctantly, Washington pushed the man away and watched him disappear into the dark. "That sort of thing can't hurt us," John Roebling went on. "We're building a good bridge, and people will realize that soon enough. As for these Know-Nothings, they're getting desperate. Since their party split on the slavery issue, they've become nothing but a hate organization."

"And all the talk against the bridge?" asked Washington.

"I hear it in town, around the boarding house, everywhere. People resent the fact that it's going to be a toll bridge."

"I know. But that's the Directors' problem. My concern is the construction—that's all."

Washington spent much of the time during the next few months standing on top of the towers, supervising the cable-spinning. Signaling to assistants on the catwalk below and on shore, he made sure that the sag of each strand was exactly right. He smiled to himself, remembering how he had crouched so fear-fully at the top of the Niagara tower that long-ago day. Now he could negotiate the swaying catwalk or windy towers easily. He gloried in his strength, the work itself, and even the hazards.

A few days before Christmas, Washington received a package from his mother with a sweater she had knit for him and a wistful note in German. Johanna Roebling had never learned to read and write English, although she could speak it. Washington read the note with a growing feeling of guilt. She wondered whether it might not be possible for them to get away for a few days and come home for the holidays. Willie was sick again, and the other children would so like to see their father and brother.

Washington remembered vividly his own resentment on those many Christmases that his father had been away. At the same time, he knew they could not go. The weather was good; the work had to go on. He wrote back as kindly and cheerfully as he could, promising to make a long visit in the spring.

When the cables had been spun and wrapped, they hung the suspenders that would support the floor of the bridge. Then in February they were ready to begin constructing the roadway. The weather was unbelievably warm and sunny. One day Washington was able to go out on the footbridge in his shirt-sleeves. When he got back to shore he looked at the thermometer and saw that it was sixty-five degrees. He was surprised to see his father study-ing the sky anxiously.

20

"What's the matter?" asked Washington.

"The temperature went up too fast. It was near freezing last night. The wind is changing—and see those clouds piling up in the northwest?"

Washington went back to work and dismissed his father's concern. But an hour later he noticed a sudden chill in the breeze. By the end of the day the sky was cloudy and the wind was blowing strongly out of the north.

"I don't like the look of things," his father said. "I think we'd better stay here tonight."

The snow began to fall near midnight, and soon the air was thick with it. The Roeblings sat shivering in the office, watching the storm helplessly. Not the snow or the cold but the wind with its ever-growing intensity threatened the bridge. Sometime during the night they went out to the anchorage.

Washington watched as the bridge bucked and pitched like a wild horse in the wind. The plank floor had not yet been laid, nor had the stays been put up, and it looked as though the footbridge would be torn to pieces. Possibly the whole structure would crumble and disappear beneath the whitecaps on the Allegheny.

They did what they could to ward off disaster, tightening the temporary stays, covering the equipment, and tying down everything light enough to be blown away. Still, it was morning before they knew the cables would hold.

"I can't believe it!" said Washington, slumped in a chair in the office. "I wouldn't have thought anything could hold up against that wind, especially with the bridge only half done."

"Now you know why it's so important to use good wire. Of course, when we get the floor laid and the stays up, it won't vibrate like that in the wind. But even so, as it is, there's almost no damage."

"This should stop all that talk about the bridge being unsafe.

If it could stand up to that storm I'm sure normal traffic can't hurt it."

When spring came in earnest, they were putting up wrought-iron trusses to give added stiffness to the bridge floor. More than eighty men were working on the crew now, adding the stays, taking down the footbridge, and generally finishing off the great Allegheny bridge.

Then another letter came from Washington's mother. Willie had died—little Will, always a sickly child, yet so pathetically uncomplaining. Recurring pneumonia had finally been too much for him. John Roebling started for home the next morning, but still Washington had to stay in Pittsburgh to supervise the building of the tollhouses.

The joy had gone out of the work, and Washington was not sorry when the day came for him to return to Trenton. Even the prospect of going back to the factory for a while did not bother him. At least he would be able to spend some time with his mother and the children, perhaps make up in some small measure for the grief and loneliness of the past winter. He vowed to himself that when he had a family of his own, he would find a way to keep them together.

Washington stood on the bank of the Allegheny with his bag in one hand and looked back at the bridge. It was as beautiful in its own way as the Niagara bridge, yet the two were quite different. This bridge had four spans instead of one, divided by the three granite towers. There was no doubt about its strength. Washington remembered how it had stood the force of the gale and thought of all the safety measures they had added since then.

Where would he be next summer? Washington wondered. Probably in Cincinnati, where the Ohio River bridge begun by his father had been left incomplete because of a lack of funds. The work there had been stopped in 1857, but there was talk of resuming it now. Or he might still be at the factory in Trenton. But you could never tell.

He glanced at the headline in the newspaper he had bought that morning:

SOUTHERNERS BOLT DEMOCRATIC PARTY
Breckinridge Nominated By Slave States

In the story, Congressman Alexander Stephens of Georgia was quoted as saying that "men will be cutting one another's throats in a little while. In less than twelve months we shall be in a war, and that the bloodiest in history."

The Allegheny Suspension Bridge at Pittsburgh, Pennsylvania, which was completed in 1860.

3   bridges and bullets

Lieutenant Washington Roebling looked at the big logs with disgust. Weeks ago he had ordered a carload of floor planking for the bridge he was building at Harper's Ferry, two inches by twelve inches. The wood which had finally arrived was *twelve* by twelve inch logs, and instead of one carload there were five!

"We'll keep warm this winter, anyway," his aide remarked. "Ought to make good firewood."

"How can they expect to win this war when we can't even get one simple bridge built?" Washington raged. "First they couldn't deliver the wire; then it was the timber trusses. And the men they gave us to build the thing! Prisoners, who'd like nothing better than to see it collapse into the river with a troop of Union soldiers marching across! And now this. I'd like to get my hands on the clerk who fouled up the order."

Washington stalked away from the platform of the railroad station, reliving in his mind all the frustrations of his year and a half in the Engineer Corps. He had enlisted to help put down the rebellion and fight Confederates. Instead it seemed he had spent most of the time fighting northerners! It had been the same when he had built a suspension bridge over the Rappahannock a year earlier: inadequate supplies, untrained labor, constant bickering.

Looking back, it seemed to him that his whole Army career had been wasted. He had spent the first months designing bridges that had never been built or building bridges that were never used. Knowing as he did the incredible blunders that could paralyze a handful of engineers, he wondered how many of the defeats of the war had been caused by the same sort of stupidity. Bull Run, South Mountain, Antietam—had some careless clerk or quarrelsome officer created those disasters as well?

Washington's mood did not lift when he got back to the bridge. A cold rain had started, and the sullen prisoners were huddled around a fire instead of working. The bridge looked depressingly ugly, with its wooden towers squatting in the Shenandoah. Washington thought of the graceful Allegheny bridge and sighed. He hoisted one of the prisoners to his feet and said:

"You men were supposed to be hanging the suspenders. I've marked where they go on the cables."

"We ain't about to go swinging out on those cables in this weather," the prisoner drawled. "That wind'd blow us clear to New York—and we figure we're far enough north already!" The other prisoners laughed and remained where they were.

"Maybe you'd rather be sent to one of our prison camps," Washington retorted. "Then you'd really see the north—from behind barbed wire!"

Just then a courier came running up. "Message for Lieutenant Roebling," he said, and handed Washington a sealed envelope. Washington left his assistant in charge and hurried to his tent to read the contents.

Lt. Washington A. Roebling, Harper's Ferry, Va.:

As soon as you have completed the bridge you are supervising at Harper's Ferry, report for duty to General Headquarters of the Army of the Potomac.

Gouvernour K. Warren, Chief Engineer
December 12, 1862.

So he was to join General Warren's staff! Washington did not know whether to be elated or depressed. He had heard how miserable life could be at staff headquarters, with the competition between ambitious officers and the constant arguing over strategy. Still, it was a chance to be in the thick of things, to see what was really going on in this war. Warren had a reputation as an able and conscientious officer. Washington decided to wait and see.

It was February before he had put the finishing touches on his work at Harper's Ferry and arrived at General Headquarters beside the Rappahannock in Virginia. He spent the next few months slogging through the mud created by the spring rain, and supervising the building of roads and pontoon bridges where they were needed. The Army of the Potomac was discouraged after the defeats of the fall, but morale was higher since dashing Joe Hooker had replaced Burnside as commanding general.

Washington saw General Hooker often that spring, and it was easy to understand his appeal. He was young, handsome, cocksure—just the sort of man to get the Army moving again. Yet Washington was suspicious of the boastful young general. Nobody should be *that* confident after what had happened in the previous battles.

Washington had no such doubts about General Warren, the Chief of the Engineer Corps. Warren was only about ten years his senior, and the two engineers liked and respected each other from the beginning.

G. K. Warren was not particularly attractive in looks: he was small and thin, with long black hair and a moustache. But Washington found him to be considerate, courteous, and a man of extremely good judgment.

With the end of April, the Army of the Potomac went marching off to battle again. Listening to the roar of the big guns around Chancellorsville, Washington chafed at his duties behind the

lines. He knew it was important to see that the supply and am-
munition trains got through to the Union troops, but the suspense was almost unbearable. What was going on in that smoking
wood?

It was evening before they knew: it had happened again. The
battered Union Army withdrew across the river, bested by the
Confederates again in spite of Hooker's predictions of a great
victory.

General Warren had been in the thick of it, with Hooker's
staff. "I doubt that half our men got into the battle," he told
Washington afterward. "The surprise attack seemed to paralyze
Hooker. And it wasn't all his fault, either. The great weakness of
our Army is that many of the corps commanders are just plain
incompetent."

Washington nodded. "I know a lot of them got their rank
through political pull and don't know the first thing about leading an Army Corps. It's like the men who sometimes get control
of engineering projects because they 'know the right people.'"

"Exactly! I've seen it many times. Some idiot holds the purse
strings on a railroad or bridge or building and has no idea what
the engineer is talking about. Sometimes I think all our problems
would be solved if we could just do away with the political 'pay-
off.' Well, most of them, anyway."

One morning, a few weeks after the battle, Washington
brought some papers to headquarters for General Warren to sign.
While he was waiting, a Union scout was escorted into the room
to report on his mission. Hooker and the rest of the staff were
having breakfast in the commanding general's tent, so Warren
received the message as ranking officer.

"We captured a rebel balloon!" the scout told him proudly.
"Shot a hole in it, but that can be patched up easy."

"How many men were in it?" Warren asked.

"Just one, and he got away. It came down half a mile from

Washington Roebling as a private in the Civil War.

us; the wind was blowing the wrong way. By the time we got there, he was gone."

"Well, it could be useful," said the general. "But we'd have to have a good man in it, one with sharp eyes and enough intelligence to understand what he sees. . . ."

"Sir?" Washington spoke for the first time.

"Yes, Roebling?"

"I'd like to try it."

"You? But you're an engineer, and this is a job for a scout."

"But there really isn't anything for us engineers to do here until the Army moves again. My specialty is building bridges, and we won't need a bridge right now, and . . ."

"And you're getting bored."

"Well, yes, but I do think I could be the man you want. I'm used to working at the top of bridge towers or swinging along the cables; heights don't bother me. A man who'd never been up that high might get so dizzy he wouldn't see a thing."

28

"You have a point there," said Warren thoughtfully. "All right, try it for a few days at least." He told the scout to take Washington to the captured balloon and help him patch it up.

Every morning for the next week Washington ascended in his balloon, keeping it moored at the farthest point of the Union lines so that it would not drift away. With a telescope he had a fairly good view of the Confederate camp—clear enough to tell him that there was a great deal of activity going on. He became convinced that the rebels were planning to move, but he had no clue as to their destination.

He made his last balloon ascent on a bright, warm day near the end of June. There was a fairly stiff breeze, and he debated with himself before going up. Finally he decided to risk it. Judging from the scurrying and loading he had seen yesterday, he sensed that this might be the day for the Confederates to break camp.

When the balloon reached the end of its rope, Washington took out his telescope. The basket swayed so much that he could not keep it to his eye at first, but at last he steadied his arm and got a glimpse of the camp. What he saw made him blink and look again. The rebels were gone!

Squinting in the bright sunlight, he could make out a few columns of soldiers marching away. But where were they going? The answer to that question was vital, he knew. There had been so much misinformation hindering the Army that this time the generals had to know the truth.

The wind was blowing in the general direction of the rebel march. Washington hesitated, then drew his knife and cut the rope.

He was not prepared for the jerk with which the balloon, freed from its mooring, sailed away. Dropping his telescope to the bottom of the basket, he gripped the sides with both hands.

The landscape below him was lush and beautiful, with its

farms and woods and streams. This part of Virginia had not yet been devastated by the war. Then he saw the rebels in their full strength, and there could be no doubt of the direction of the march. They were moving northwest, toward the Shenandoah Valley and the Potomac. Unless this was an elaborate ruse and Lee intended to swing around in a new path, the conclusion was obvious: the Confederates were planning to cross into Pennsylvania.

Now Washington had to get down and back to the Union lines. He pulled the balloon's plug, and the air began whooshing out of it. The basket swayed crazily, then began a fairly steady descent. Washington crouched in the bottom and held on tightly, waiting for the inevitable crash.

It did not come. Instead, he felt the motion stop gently and heard only a light scratching sound. He stood up and saw that the balloon was caught in the limbs of a big old tree, the basket dangling feebly below. Once again Washington was glad for his experience in climbing around on bridge cables. He shinnied up the balloon ropes to a large limb, swung along it to the trunk and slid down.

He was in a large meadow, with a glade of trees at the edge of it. Though he was sure that the rebels must have seen the balloon, he hoped at first that they had not bothered to send a patrol after him. Then a rifle cracked, and the bullet kicked up dust only a few yards from him. He started across the meadow at a dead run.

Bullets whizzed around him, and he waited for the impact of one on his body. Somehow he reached the shelter of the trees. He looked back and saw a half dozen graycoats running toward him, their rifles smoking. But they had stopped to take aim, and he had a good headstart on them. He ran on toward the Union lines, his lungs burning and his legs growing weaker with every step.

He leaped across a tiny stream and stumbled. Lying in the mud, gasping, he waited for the rebels to catch up with him. Then he heard a gruff voice:

"Hold still or you'll never get up again. Who are you?"

It was a Union sentry.

"I'm a scout from General Warren's staff. I have to see him right away—I've got important information." The sentry was suspicious at first, but he finally allowed Washington to pass into the camp.

Washington's report, together with others from scouting parties and civilians, confirmed the direction of the rebel movement and set the Army of the Potomac in motion again. If Lee was marching into Pennsylvania, they would be there to meet him in full force.

As they prepared to break camp, the General Staff discovered that they did not have an accurate map of Pennsylvania! Hooker stormed at the inefficiency of the War Department, and Washington remembered that his father had an excellent map of the state. John Roebling had used it in his work on the Pennsylvania Canal, and Washington had seen it in the office at Trenton many times. So he was sent home to get it, going by train when possible and getting rides the rest of the way.

"Son!" His mother wept when she saw him. He was not sure whether she cried for joy or because of the way he looked. He had had little sleep since that balloon trip five days before, his clothes were stiff with dirt, and his face was hidden behind a brush of untrimmed beard.

"I can't stay, Mother. I came for a map of Father's. Is he here?"

Johanna Roebling shook her head. "He's in Kentucky. They're starting work on that bridge from Cincinnati to Covington again."

Washington bathed, ate a huge meal, and took a nap while

his mother and sisters washed and dried his clothes and packed him a lunch. He played with the children, answered the boys' questions about the war, and tried vainly to cheer his mother. She did not look well, and she had aged terribly in the two years he had been away.

It was evening when he set out, the map carefully folded in his pack. He had taken one of the family's saddle horses, for he was not sure just where he would find the Army, and trains would be of no help on this trip. He rode all night, crossing from New Jersey to Pennsylvania some time before dawn.

Passing through the rich "Pennsylvania Dutch" country, he watched constantly for either of the two armies that were coming this way. He slept in a cave one night, a haystack the second.

Early on the morning of July 1, 1863, Washington rode down from the northeast toward a little town called Gettysburg. With great relief he saw bluecoated soldiers in the streets, and he had just spurred his horse to cover the remaining distance when he heard from the hills west of town the rattle of rifle fire.

Washington found nothing but confusion in and around Gettysburg. He asked for Hooker's headquarters, only to be told that Hooker was no longer in command. General Meade was now in charge of the Army—and Meade and his staff had not arrived yet. Washington borrowed a rifle from one of the wounded men who were already being brought back to town and fell in with a German regiment that was moving to defend the area from the advancing rebels.

The next three days were blurred in his mind even as he lived them. When General Meade's staff arrived, he was put to work as a courier. Once he and General Warren climbed the hill called "Little Round Top" to get a view of the battle and saw to their horror that the Union line had broken. They dashed down the hill, stopped the first Union brigade they saw, and rushed them back up the hill just in time to meet the Confederates who were charging up the other side.

Another time Washington was studying a map in General Headquarters when a shell burst through the window and knocked two legs off the table. The cottage was rocked by explosion after explosion, with shells smashing through the roof and door. General Meade finally decided that the whole staff should move outside where at least there was less danger from flying glass and splinters.

When the Confederates made their last desperate charge, Washington moved to the front and fired until his rifle was red-hot. Then it was over; the enemy disappeared, the thundering cannon stopped, and Washington was amazed to hear a bird singing.

He looked around. Dead and wounded were everywhere, rebels and yankees together in some places. General Warren appeared, one hand pressed to his neck and blood trickling between the fingers.

"You're hurt?" Washington asked stupidly.

"Just a flesh wound. How about you?"

Washington hesitated, still numb from the long exertion. He looked down at himself, moved his hands over his arms and legs.

He was not even scratched.

4 the general's sister

Through the battles that followed—the campaign around Richmond, the Battle of the Wilderness, Spottsylvania, Petersburg—Washington saw regular action, serving more as an infantryman than an engineer. And in all that time he was never wounded.

General Warren took over as commander of the V Corps, and the young engineer went along, serving as courier, assistant, and confidant. The more fighting he saw and the closer his escapes, the less Washington feared death or injury. Time after time, he stood in the thick of battle, with men dropping all around him, and remained unhurt.

Once he came into Meade's headquarters and found it empty. Just about to leave, he noticed that a diary kept by one of the staff had been left open on the table. He glanced at it, saw his name, and was unable to resist the temptation to read the description of him that the man had written:

> *Roebling is a character. . . . A light-haired, blue-eyed man, with a countenance as if all the world were an empty show. He stoops a good deal, when riding has the stirrups so long that the tips of his toes can just touch them; and, as he wears no boots, the bottoms of his pantaloons are always torn and ragged.*

He goes poking about in the most dangerous places, looking for the position of the enemy, and always with an air of entire indifference. His conversation is curt and not garnished with polite turnings.

So that was how he appeared to others! It was hard for Washington to see himself in that blunt description; yet he supposed it was fair enough. He had heard fellow soldiers refer to him as "cold-blooded," or the more friendly ones to praise him for his courage. He did not think of himself as courageous or cold-blooded, either. It was simply that for some reason he did not believe he was going to be hurt. But that night he did mend his pantaloons and shorten his stirrup straps.

It was the spring of 1864, and the Union Army had another new commander. The soldiers had seen too many generals come and go to have much enthusiasm for Ulysses S. Grant.

One bright morning Washington brought General Warren's mail and stayed to chat while the General glanced through it.

"No!" Warren exclaimed suddenly. "That Emily!" Washington maintained a polite silence, but the General seemed to feel that he should explain. "It's one of my sisters. She's coming down here! On her way right now, according to this! Has some crazy notion about being a nurse or something."

"If the rumors are true about our fighting again soon, there may be a need . . ."

"Nonsense!" Warren barked in an unusual display of temper. "You know what those field hospitals are like. No place for respectable young women."

"I have heard that after Gettysburg many ladies from good families helped with the nursing." Washington did not know why he was defending this unknown sister; he had no desire to get involved in a family quarrel.

Warren sighed. "You don't know my sister. She's not—well,

she's not the usual sort of girl. Over twenty already, and not married, not even an offer as far as I know."

A picture formed in Washington's mind of a revoltingly ugly girl with warts and a long, crooked nose.

As though reading his mind, Warren went on: "It's not that she isn't attractive. She's just never learned to stay in her place! Too educated, for one thing. When the family wouldn't let her go to school any more, she kept up on her own, borrowing books, even reading mine on the sly. Imagine a girl wanting to know about engineering!"

They shared a manly laugh at the idea of a female who thought she could comprehend the complexities of mathematics and construction.

"She's a good girl, really," said Warren, "and I'll admit she's quite intelligent. But, after all, what man wants to marry a woman who knows as much as he does?"

"Well, I don't know," mused Washington. "It might be more interesting than spending the rest of your life with one of these fluttering, empty-headed types."

"Maybe you're right. I do think Emily'd make a fine wife if she'd just get rid of some of these notions of hers! Today it's nursing; tomorrow she'll want to be a bookkeeper or an actress or who knows what! I think that Dorothea Dix and the other feminists ought to be clapped in jail—filling young girls' heads with ideas about women's rights and whatnot!"

Now Washington had a new picture of Emily Warren. He could see her quite clearly: tall, rawboned, with her hair drawn back severely and her sharp features set in an expression of determination.

"Good heavens!" Warren exclaimed. "The train she's taking gets in today! And I have a hundred things to attend to. Why couldn't she give me some warning? Just like her! Roebling, would you do me a favor and meet her at the station, find her some sort of room? I'll try to see her later on."

An hour later Washington watched the train pull in. As the passengers got off he looked for a woman fitting the picture he had imagined, but it soon became obvious that no one of that description was on the train. There was only one woman—a girl, really—and she was small, delicate, and very pretty.

Washington approached her uncertainly. "Miss, excuse me, would you be Emily Warren?"

"Yes, did my brother send you?"

Washington stared at her, unable to reconcile this lovely creature with the brainy feminist General Warren had described.

"I can see Gouv told you about me." She laughed. "Did you expect me to be an Amazon or something?"

This was so close to the truth that Washington could feel himself blushing.

They talked as he escorted her to the rooming house in the little town. He found himself doing most of the talking as she questioned him about his experiences and his work. She seemed especially interested in the bridges he had built.

"Thank you, Lieutenant Roebling," she told him after he had made the arrangements for her room. "I hope I'll see you again before I leave. I suppose Gouv will be sending me back in a few days."

"You're not going to become a nurse?"

"I don't think I can talk him into it. He's the oldest boy, and, you know, he can be something of a fussbudget. He's awfully old-fashioned when it comes to 'a woman's place.' How many sermons I've had on *that* subject! I'm going to try to convince him that as a nurse I can contribute something to the country, too—but I suppose he'll just shake his head and ship me back."

"I'm sure it's only because he's concerned for you."

"Yes, I know, but his idea of making me happy is to fit me into a mold. It isn't that I want to be a man—I just want to be me! Is that asking so much?"

"Well, uh . . ." Washington did not know how to answer her.

"I'm sorry," she said quickly. "See, here I am, doing just what Gouv says I shouldn't—lecturing a man, and one I've just met at that! Forgive me, and if you aren't completely disgusted with me, I'd like to see that bridge you mentioned you were building near here. Do you think you could find time in the next day or two?"

"Yes, if you want to see it. It really isn't much of a bridge; the Rappahannock's just a stream up here. But I could take you out there tomorrow morning, if you like. Right after breakfast?"

Washington borrowed a wagon for the short ride to the bridge. It was midmorning by the time they got there, and as Washington helped Emily down, he thought again how small and light she was, how unlike what he had expected.

It was a perfect spring day, and Washington only wished the bridge did not look so ordinary and drab against the brilliant colors of the Virginia landscape.

"It's just a footbridge," he explained. "The Army isn't much interested in beauty—only in getting troops and supplies over the river."

"But is that what they call a suspension bridge, like the one you mentioned your father built at Niagara Falls? Tell me, what is a suspension bridge?"

Washington thought a moment, trying to boil down his years of technical training into a simple explanation. "It's like the difference between a hammock and a chair. The chair sits on the floor; the legs hold the weight. But a hammock hangs between two trees. It's *suspended,* and the weight is held by the supports to which it's tied."

"I see! An ordinary bridge is built on piers, like chair legs. But with a suspension bridge you build a tower on each bank and then hang the bridge between them like a hammock! Of course, that makes more sense—you don't clutter up the river with all those piers. I'll bet it costs less, too. Why didn't anyone think of it before?"

Washington was amazed at her quick understanding of the suspension bridge principle. This girl really was intelligent. "It isn't new," he told her. "When primitive men used to swing across a river on a vine, that was a suspension bridge. And many early civilizations had bridges of ropes or cables tied to trees. The problem with suspension bridges is making them stiff enough. I read somewhere that on those early rope bridges the passengers often crossed blindfolded because they swayed so frighteningly."

"But your father's bridges are strong enough even for trains, aren't they? And this one looks steady." Emily walked out on the bridge and leaned over the side. "Is it these cables that hold it?"

Washington spent the rest of the morning answering Emily's questions. Two things impressed him about her: her comprehension of the things he told her and her eagerness to learn. After taking her back to the rooming house and returning the wagon, he walked back toward his tent, unable to get the General's sister out of his mind. He could see why Warren worried about her and why men might shy away from her in spite of her beauty and charm. Women just were not supposed to be interested in suspension bridges and such!

The next day, at General Warren's request, he escorted Emily back to the station and put her on the train to New York. Impulsively, he asked her to write to him when she got home, and she promised.

In the following weeks Washington had little time to think about Emily Warren. Grant led his troops south, into a tangle of trees and brush where the Confederates were, and the Battle of the Wilderness began. Washington fought with Warren's troops, stumbling blindly through the undergrowth, firing whenever he got a glimpse of the enemy. Once more Washington came through without even a flesh wound.

He was Major Roebling now, and through the summer of 1864 he followed the trail blazed by Grant, Meade, Warren, and the Union Army into the south. He and Emily exchanged frequent letters. In August she visited the camp again, during a lull in the fighting. Though she was supposedly visiting her brother, Washington took up most of her time for the ten days she was there.

In November an unexpected letter arrived from John Roebling. Washington had not corresponded with his father in the three years since he left Trenton to enlist. He opened the letter fearfully.

> *Son: I regret very much having to tell you that your mother died last Tuesday, November 22, at 12:30 P.M. As you know, she has not been well for some time. I was able to get home before the end came. . . .*

"Good for you!" Washington thought savagely. "Too bad she had to die to get you home for a few days!" Then he read on.

> *Johanna was one of those rare people who think only of others. You knew her unselfishness, patience and kindness as well as I did. My only regret is that I never appreciated her as I should have. . . .*

Father with regrets—that was out of character. But maybe he really was sorry for all the years of neglect. Maybe guilt would haunt him for a long time.

Washington glanced at the picture of Emily that he kept on his table, and suddenly he understood the tragedy of his parents' marriage. They had had nothing in common but their children.

Emily Warren Roebling.

For some people that might have been enough, but John Roebling was obsessed with his bridges. Johanna had known nothing about them and had not been really interested, except as they had affected her relationship with her husband. She had had no desire to pack up the family and move to a new bridge site every year or two. She had wanted a home, roots, friends.

Emily Warren was different. With a woman like her, he could share the dreams—and the problems—of building bridges. He could keep his family together, and he would not have to be torn apart by conflicting loyalties. Besides, he realized that he could not imagine his life without Emily. Had he fallen in love with her that first day or at the bridge, when he had recognized her quick intelligence, or on her second visit to Virginia? He was not sure, and it didn't matter. He took a fresh sheet of paper from his notebook and began to write:

> *Dearest Emily: Of all the ways in which a man can propose marriage, I suppose a letter is the least romantic. . . .*

Colonel Washington Roebling was discharged from the Union Army in January, 1865. He went immediately to Cold Spring, New York, and he and Emily were married there on January 18. General Warren came back for the wedding, but of course John Roebling could not leave Kentucky, where he was working on the Cincinnati-Covington bridge. He wired his son to join him as soon as possible, so Washington and Emily took their wedding trip on the way to Kentucky.

At first Washington sensed his father's disapproval of Emily's presence—a distraction! But after a few weeks he seemed to accept her, for Washington worked as well as ever and she did not interfere. Emily, for her part, was careful to stay away from the bridge. She explored Cincinnati, made friends, and kept their rooms shining and cheerful. On a few warm evenings Washington took her to the bridge after work and explained what was going on.

To him, this bridge was the most beautiful thing in the world, with its great towers so high that a man had to crane his neck to see the top. More than that, it was a symbol of all he had fought for. In his mind it stood for the Union itself, soaring over the Ohio River between North and South.

But the wound was not yet healed, and in Virginia the war went on. March came with news of a battle near a little spot called Dinwiddie Court House, near Five Forks. Then there was a letter from G. K. Warren, with the incredible news that General Sheridan had removed him from command of the V Corps! Sheridan accused him of being too slow in getting his men into the fight. Warren was indignant. He told them he had plenty of evidence that the charges were unjust, that his orders had been confusing, and that he had not had proper maps.

"That's ridiculous!" said Washington when he read the letter. "When I think of some of the blunders I saw early in the war; and the commanders responsible were promoted, not removed! Sheridan has a reputation for being hot-tempered; I suppose he just jumped to the wrong conclusion and then wouldn't back down."

"But can't Gouv clear himself?" Emily asked.

"I'm not sure. He'll try everything, of course—military review boards, articles in the papers, letters to congressmen—but I'm afraid he may just have to live with it in the end. He'll be fighting Army red tape and the publicity in the papers when Sheridan's charges are published. Red tape and public opinion—it's hard to beat that combination!"

The war ended less than two weeks later, and in the celebration no one seemed much interested in the pleas of Gouverneur K. Warren that he had been removed from command unjustly. After all, only his reputation was at stake, and this was peacetime. Washington wrote letters on Warren's behalf to everyone he knew with influence in the Army, but nothing came of it.

On the first day of December, 1866, the Ohio River Bridge was opened. Newspapers hailed it as the longest single-span bridge in the world. At sunrise a squad from the nearby Newport Barracks fired a salute with a hundred cannon, and then the crowds streamed across. Sitting beside the saddle, high at the top of the Cincinnati tower, Washington watched them through a telescope. In the very first group he could make out the figure of a small dark-haired young woman in a green dress—Emily!

After the formal opening there was still a little work to be done—painting, finishing the sidewalks and railings, putting up the gaslights. This work went slowly, for 1866-67 was one of the worst winters in the country's history.

One cold evening in February John Roebling brought Washington a newspaper with a story which he had circled:

DEMAND GROWS FOR BRIDGE OVER EAST RIVER

Rumors persist that a bill will be introduced in the New York legislature this spring to authorize the building of a bridge over the East River from New York to Brooklyn. Meanwhile, thousands of New Yorkers are unable to get in or out of the city because the river is choked with ice. It has been observed that one can go from Albany to Brooklyn in less time than it takes to get across the East River by ferry. If public pressure continues, it seems certain that prominent engineers will be asked to submit plans. . . .

"A bridge over the East River!" said Washington. "You think we might . . . ?"

"I wrote to Abram Hewitt ten years ago with some ideas about that!" John Roebling's dark eyes glittered. "It has to be a suspension bridge, of course. That river has heavy traffic; no room for a lot of piers. But the foundations will have to be in the river. Have you some paper, Washington? I want to sketch some rough plans. . . ."

5   new bridges in old europe

On an April evening three months later John Roebling had supper at his son's flat, a sort of farewell party that Emily had suggested. He was leaving the next day for New York to begin preliminary plans for a bridge over the East River.

"Do you think you'll get the appointment as Chief Engineer?" Washington asked him when Emily was serving their after-dinner coffee.

"I'm sure of it," John said flatly. "I've had correspondence with several of the incorporators, and they can't see it as anything but a suspension bridge."

"And you're the only American engineer who has built large, successful suspension bridges," said Emily.

"I still have to draw the plans, of course. There will be some special problems that I've never dealt with before." John Roebling hesitated, then went on slowly. "I couldn't do it without you, Washington. I'm not young, and this bridge will take years to build. If they do accept my plans, I'll take it only on condition that you be hired as my chief assistant."

"Naturally I'll work on the bridge with you," said Washington, "if they offer me the job."

"You're trained and experienced; you'll be taking your own projects soon. As a matter of fact, you could probably build this bridge yourself. I'd say you're the only other engineer in America who could. Anyway, there's something I'd like you to do for me as soon as we're finished here—say, the end of June. I want you to go to Europe and have a look at some of the things they're building there. Especially the compressed air work—I think we're going to have to try that method to sink our foundations, and it's never been done in America. Take Emily along; call it a delayed honeymoon trip, a gift from me. I don't think I ever gave you a wedding present, did I?"

Washington and Emily stared at each other. A trip to Europe! They had dreamed of such a thing, but had assumed that it would be years before Washington had either the time or the money. Now, there was another problem. . . .

When John Roebling had left, Emily took both Washington's hands and danced across the room with him. "Isn't it marvelous?"

"Yes, but, Em, what about the baby?"

"People have babies in Europe, don't they? Your father was born there; is there any reason why his first grandchild shouldn't be?"

Washington shook his head. "I don't know—there's the boat trip over, and then traveling all around, staying in strange places. I don't think Father would approve of your going if he knew."

"So we won't tell him. We'll write him a letter." Emily's eyes flashed. "Washington Augustus Roebling, if you think I'm going to miss out on this trip. . . ."

"All right, all right." He laughed. "You're too much for me, as usual!"

John Roebling was appointed Chief Engineer of the East River Bridge on May 23, 1867. Early in July Washington and Emily sailed for France. The boat trip was pleasant enough, and the weather was good, but Washington grew bored before it was over. He tried to sit on the deck chairs and relax, but he would find himself staring up at the smokestack and calculating how high a bridge would have to be for it to clear. He spent part of the time reading European scientific journals, particularly those which mentioned the new method of digging bridge foundations and tunnels in pneumatic caissons.

"What are these caissons, and how do they work?" Emily asked him one afternoon when she found him engrossed in one of his journals.

"A caisson is just a watertight box with an open bottom," Washington told her. "When it's put into the river, air is pumped into it, and this drives the water out. It rests against the floor of the river, and then men can work inside it to dig the foundation for the towers."

"That sounds simple enough. Why hasn't it been done?"

"There are a lot of problems. First, you have to be sure the caisson is really watertight. Then the air pressure has to be great enough to keep water from rushing in around the bottom. And scientists aren't sure yet just how that much air pressure will affect men who work in the caissons."

"You mean it might be dangerous?"

"Possibly. These caissons work on the same principle as diving bells, and men who go down in those to great depths have had a bad reaction to the pressure—something they call the 'bends.' It's very painful and sometimes fatal."

"But then why don't you just use the same methods as before? Why try this?"

"These towers will have to be too wide for the old cofferdam system. Besides, we may have to dig a long way to reach a solid foundation. They say the bottom of that river is very uneven, with a lot of mud, sand, and quicksand; no one knows how deep we'll have to go to find bedrock."

"I suppose that's why no one has built a bridge between New

47

York and Brooklyn before this," Emily said. "I know people have talked about it for years."

"There's been some experimentation since Sir Thomas Cochrane first invented the caisson in 1830, by engineers like Brunel, Seguin, St.-Denis, and Audernt. But it's been mostly in shallow tunnels and viaducts or in combination with traditional methods used on bridges. Caissons really haven't been tested enough to prove how the compressed air affects men in deep excavations."

They spent August and September traveling through France and Switzerland. Emily enjoyed seeing the countryside while Washington inspected engineering projects. He was particularly interested in the early suspension bridges built by the famous French engineer, Seguin, and by the examples of caisson excavation that he found.

When they crossed into Germany, Washington could communicate easily with the fluent German he had learned at home. It was a relief not to have to rely on Emily's schoolgirl French when trying to talk with someone. Washington visited the famous Krupp steel works and spent several days studying their manufacturing techniques. The Roeblings were almost sure that they wanted to use this new metal for the wire cables of the East River bridge.

In Berlin, Washington saw the Royal Polytechnic Institute where his father had been trained as an engineer. Then in early November they set out for Mulhouse, the Roebling family's ancestral home, located in an area that through the ages had been shunted between France and Germany. It was now a part of France, but the Roebling relatives were of German origin. Washington and Emily first saw the walls of Mulhouse through a fine, misty rain as the train rattled toward it.

"I remember Father telling me this city is a thousand years old," said Washington, trying to add some color to the bleak surroundings. He felt excited and a little nervous at the thought of seeing his father's birthplace. The grandparents he had never known were buried there and their fathers and grandfathers. This place had shaped his life, his character, even while he was growing up in Pennsylvania and New Jersey.

"A thousand years old," said Emily thoughtfully. "I can't get used to the age of these European cities. In New York, we thought a pre-Revolutionary house was really historic! Those walls do look forbidding."

"I don't think they protected the city as well as the builders hoped. When Father was a boy, Napoleon's armies marched through—and then, after they'd been defeated, the Swedes, the Austrians, and Prussians came. . . ."

Just then the train passed through an opening in the wall and groaned to a stop. They were met on the platform by several cousins with whom Washington had corresponded for years. The cousins took them to an inn just across the street from the Roebling home on Erfurterstrasse.

The time in Mulhouse flew by, as they visited with the many branches of the family and heard endless stories about little John. It amused Washington to hear tales of his father's childish pranks. Washington had never been able to picture John Roebling as a boy; it seemed almost as if John had been born a grown man, with a beard! But now he looked at his father's baby clothes, saw the rooms and streets where he had played, and the gulf between them closed slightly in his mind.

The German Roeblings remembered John best as a young man, in the years just before he had migrated to America.

"That boy was always a dreamer," recalled an old uncle. "It wasn't enough for him to study engineering at the Institute—he had to go over to the University of Berlin at the same time and take courses in philosophy!"

"Was that when Hegel was his teacher?" asked Washington.

"Ah, yes! For a year or so all we heard from John was 'Herr Hegel says . . .' or 'according to Professor Hegel . . .'"

"Then that friend of his, Etzler, got him interested in going to America," said a cousin. "They were full of plans for some sort of cooperative settlement there. 'A new world!' John would say. 'Just waiting for us to make it perfect!' He was tired of all the government restrictions in Europe, and the petty officials who were in charge of engineering projects. He was sure everything would be different in the United States—'A young country being built by young people,' he would say."

Can they be talking about my father? Washington wondered. He found it hard to recognize anything familiar in the idealistic, impetuous man his relatives were describing. Aloud, he asked, "Was that just before Father and Uncle Karl left here?"

"Yes," said the cousin. "I gather that Pennsylvania was not the paradise they had been led to expect. Do you remember much about Saxonburg?"

Washington shook his head. "Not too much. We moved to Trenton when I was ten. Saxonburg was pretty primitive, the land was poor, and I guess Father just wasn't cut out to be a farmer. When the town had been settled he lost interest in it and went back to engineering. Then he started his wire rope manufacturing, and Saxonburg was too remote for a growing business."

"I remember when your father left for America," said Washington's aunt. "He walked up the gangplank of that little ship— the *August Eduard,* it was called—without a backward glance."

Washington reflected that his father had never been interested in looking back. He had never revisited Europe; he did not go back to Saxonburg; he had no desire to return to a bridge once it had been completed. In this, at least, he had not changed.

Walking back to the inn that night, Washington told Emily of his thoughts about his father. "I just can't imagine Father the way they described him—so enthusiastic, so open-minded, so—"

"So young?" asked Emily gently. "I suppose it's hard for any of us to believe that our parents were once young and felt as we do now."

"Maybe you're right. Yes, I'm sure that's part of it. But I actually think his interest in philosophy may have had something to do with the change. I don't pretend to be a student of Hegel, but I know enough about his teachings to be suspicious of them, because they're so *complete!* They take in the whole world, nature, people, society—with a neat little slot for everything and no room for any sort of doubts."

"You think your father was influenced too much by Hegel?"

"I wonder. He talks about that manuscript of his, the 'Theory of the Universe,' as if he's absolutely sure that when it's finished he'll have said everything worth saying, and only a fool would disagree. Well, anyway, it's been interesting to hear what he was like as a boy. I only wish he'd held onto the habit of dreaming and questioning. . . ."

On Sundays they attended Lutheran services at the Church of St. Blasius, built in the twelfth century. Washington could not enter its doors or listen to its huge organ without thinking of Johann Sebastian Bach, who had been married in that church and had composed his first great cantatas there. The love of music that Washington had inherited from his father was very evident in the German branch of the Roebling family. On several occasions they put on their own musicales, and Washington was invited to join in on the violin.

Early in the morning on November 21, 1867, Washington hurried a few blocks to the home of the local doctor and brought him back to the hotel. A few hours later he had a son.

He saw them that evening, the baby a tiny scrap of humanity sleeping in the crook of his mother's arm.

"What shall we call him, Em?"

"Why, John, of course! It's only appropriate, since he was born here in Mulhouse just like his grandfather."

"I think Father would be pleased." Washington had thought of the same thing, but he had hesitated to suggest it. "Of course, we could name him after your father or your brother. . . ."

"*Gouverneur?*" Emily laughed. "No, poor Gouv has had to bear that name for a long time, and I wouldn't inflict it on this helpless little boy! And my father's name isn't much better—imagine calling him Sylvanus!"

John Augustus Roebling II was baptized at St. Blasius as his grandfather had been. A few weeks later, as soon as Emily was strong enough, they set out on the last lap of their tour—England.

There were several important bridges Washington wanted to see there. He settled Emily and the baby in London with the family of a school friend of hers and set off alone for Saltash, to see the world-famous Royal Albert Bridge. Washington was not so much interested in the construction of the bridge itself as in the foundations, for pneumatic caissons had been used to dig through the bottom of the river Tamar.

Washington spent several days there. The engineer of the

The spires of St. Blasius, Mulhouse, France.

Royal Albert, I. K. Brunel, came at Washington's request and answered his many questions about the problems of caisson work. Though the foundations of this bridge were not as deep as those of the East River bridge would have to be, the technique was the same as that the Roeblings planned to use.

"Did you have trouble with caisson disease?" Washington asked.

"We had some cases," Brunel told him, "but none too serious. The men would get cramps in their muscles soon after coming out of the caisson, and some became sick to their stomachs or fainted. But they all recovered from it. We found it helped to keep the work shifts short."

Washington visited other bridges in England—the Britannia Bridge, the Menai suspension bridge, the High Level Bridge at Newcastle—but in general he was not impressed with British engineering. One thing he felt sure was holding back the development of bridge-building there: the Board of Trade had decreed that steel could not be used in bridges. To him this ruling seemed incredibly shortsighted, made in ignorance of scientific fact, a product of superstition and unreasoning fear.

Early in the spring Washington and Emily were ready to take the boat back to New York. Little John was thriving in spite of their constant travel, and he seemed to enjoy the boat trip. He received constant attention from the passengers and crew. Washington tried to relax and enjoy this time with his wife and child. He told himself that it might be years before he would have an unbroken stretch of time like this to be with them. But he could not help being impatient to get back to New York, back to work.

John Roebling met the boat at the pier. He greeted them, looked at the baby without much enthusiasm, and then put a quick end to their holiday mood: "We've got problems, Washington."

6 roebling says so

A hired carriage took them to the brownstone rooming house where Washington and Emily would stay until they could find a house. Washington's father helped unload the luggage and carry it to their rooms while Emily put the baby to bed. For a few minutes they talked of family news—John Roebling had married again recently—and of the European trip. Then Washington asked:

"Well, what about the bridge? What's wrong?"

"We're getting some bad publicity, and even some engineers are beginning to question my plans."

"On what grounds?"

"Oh, just about everything. Some still don't believe in suspension bridges. Then I proposed the use of steel wire instead of iron; that's stirred up quite a controversy. Most of the noise against my plans is being made by Mayor Kalbfleisch of Brooklyn. . . ."

"He's afraid the bridge will take business from Brooklyn to Manhattan," Washington commented.

"Yes, I think that's behind it. But Horace Greeley has been giving us a bad time, too, and the *Tribune* is an important paper. I don't know who's convinced him that my plans are unsafe. I have heard that several engineers who wanted the commission themselves have been criticizing my ideas. They say that it can't be done, that just because no one has ever built a span this long it's impossible. I wish I knew a way to silence these rumors."

The two men tried to find a solution to the problem, but they could think of nothing better than writing a letter to send to the *Tribune*. They spent the rest of the evening trying to compose a suitable letter while Emily worked quietly beside them, unpacking and putting things away.

Suddenly Emily broke into their discussion to ask John Roebling, "Most engineers would approve of your plans if they could study them, wouldn't they?"

"Yes, I'm sure they would, but. . . "

"What if you asked the directors of the bridge company to appoint a board of engineers to go over the plans and give an opinion? If a group of the most important engineers in America approve your ideas, wouldn't that satisfy the critics?"

"It would certainly help." John Roebling stroked his beard thoughtfully.

"The newspapers would have to report the findings of a group like that," said Washington.

"Horatio Allen would make a good chairman; he's well respected." John was speaking to Washington; the two men had forgotten Emily. "We'd have to include Julius Adams."

"Adams? But he was one who wanted to design the bridge himself. I remember hearing that he submitted a plan several years before you did."

"Exactly. And he's been one of the loudest critics of my plan. That's why he has to be on the board. If he approves the plan. . . "

"But will he?"

"Adams is a reputable engineer. And I'm sure he's honest. I can convince him."

Two weeks later a board of consulting engineers was appointed, at John Roebling's request, to go over his plans. It took the seven men two months to complete their study. John and Washington met with them many times and answered their questions. Were the Roeblings sure the steel cables would be strong enough to hold more than eighteen thousand tons? Would the bridge be stable enough to resist wind damage? How did they know the foundations could be dug by the untried caisson method?

"Talk, talk, talk!" Washington exploded as he and his father left one of the meetings. "If words were bricks, we'd have both towers up by now!"

"Sometimes it takes a lot of words to get the bricks you need," said John Roebling. "That's the trouble with engineering; you always have to depend on someone else to get the material for your work."

Washington had to admit that the consulting engineers were doing their job carefully. They even traveled to Cincinnati, Pittsburgh, and Niagara to look at John Roebling's previous suspension bridges. Finally, one afternoon in May, John and Washington were invited to a luncheon meeting at the American Institute Fair Building. The engineers were ready to present their final report.

It was warm for the time of year, and Washington felt his shirt sticking to his back as they took their places around a table in the private dining room. The food tasted like Army hardtack to him; he was amazed at his own nervousness. He remembered his reputation as a "cold-blooded" soldier, and here he was, terrified of the verdict of these mild-looking engineers. He told himself he did not care what they said; the plan was good, and they would get the bridge built somehow.

The chairman, Horatio Allen, stood after the plates had been cleared and read from the sheaf of papers in his hand. He droned on about the work of the committee, the trips taken, the testimony they had heard. Washington lost the train of it for a few minutes, but his mind jumped back to attention as Allen read the conclusion of the report:

> *We believe, therefore, that it is entirely practicable to erect a steel wire suspension bridge of sixteen hundred foot span, one hundred thirty-five feet elevation across the East River, in accordance with the plans of Mr. Roebling and that such structure will have all the strength and durability that should attend the permanent connection by a bridge of the Cities of New York and Brooklyn.*

They had won! Even Adams had agreed, for the report was unanimous. Now the newspapers would have to stop printing gossip about the bridge and its "impracticality." People would be willing to invest money; the funds would be ready, and the work could begin!

"Looks like the worst is over," said Washington to his father on the way home from the meeting. "Now we should be able to get on with it. . . . "

"It's not that simple." John Roebling was not nearly so elated as his son. "Most people will say the bridge plan is all right once the report is published. But will they invest in it? Remember, it's going to cost seven million dollars or more. And private citizens just don't have that kind of money. I talked to Kingsley about it the other day, and he says he's trying to get the city governments to assume part of the cost."

"With Boss Tweed in control of New York?"

"Well, I don't know anything about politics. I leave that to the Board of Directors to worry about."

Washington said no more, but he was uneasy about the arrangements being made to finance the bridge. He had met William Kingsley and had heard him describe with obvious pride his rise from a job as clerk and bookkeeper to owner of one of the biggest contracting businesses in Brooklyn. Kingsley and the other financiers who were organizing support for the bridge were shrewd businessmen, but somehow Washington hated to think that the project depended on them.

Going up the stairs to their flat, Washington resolved to put his worries out of his mind for the moment. There wasn't much he could do about it, anyway. He knew that his capabilities lay in engineering, not finance. Ferd was the businessman of the family. Washington was glad that his younger brother had taken over at the Trenton factory.

The hall outside their flat was crowded with boxes, crates, and trunks. In a few days they were moving to a house Washington had bought in Brooklyn. He sighed, looking at the piles of possessions that would have to be moved. But it was better to do it now than after the construction of the bridge began.

When Washington went in he was surprised to see G. K. Warren sitting and talking with Emily. "Gouv!" he said with real pleasure. "I didn't know you were in town."

"Just for a few days. I had some business here, and of course I wouldn't miss the chance to see you and Emily."

They talked for a while about Warren's current job as a member of the Union Pacific Special Commission and the possibilities of his building a double-deck drawbridge at Rock Island in a year or two. Then Washington asked the inevitable question:

"How are things going with the appeal?"

Warren shook his head. "I've collected lots of testimony supporting me, but you know how government red tape is. I've made three applications for a military court to review my case— all denied. President Grant doesn't want it aired, of course. He supported Sheridan at Five Forks, and he believed I was incompetent. But I'm not going to give up. Well, enough of that. I was out at St. Louis a few months ago, Washington, and I saw something that might interest you."

"Eads' bridge?"

"Naturally! What else in St. Louis would interest you but the bridge James Eads is building over the Mississippi? It's mostly in the planning stage now, but they are getting ready to dig the foundations. That's what I thought you'd like to know. Eads is going to use pneumatic caissons."

"He is! How do you know?"

"I talked to him and saw them building the first caisson. He hopes to sink it next fall some time."

Washington felt an unreasonable pang of envy. Eads was going to use the new technique first! "What did you think of him, Gouv?" Washington asked.

"He's a genius, no doubt about that. You know he built a whole fleet of armored gunboats for the army during the war? He used to have a salvage business on the Mississippi, and he invented a diving bell, so he's had experience in working underwater. Personally—we didn't hit it off too well. He's a friend of Grant's, and I could tell he had heard some uncomplimentary things about me. He's confident—I'd say arrogant. But in spite of that I'm sure he's a fine engineer."

"I'll have to talk to him, see what he's doing, before we start caisson work. You know, my father once designed a suspension bridge to go over the Mississippi at St. Louis, but he never got financial backing for it. Eads is building an arch bridge, isn't he?"

"Yes, I saw the plans. It will have three steel arches on granite piers. By the way, I heard some good things about the East River bridge from the engineers I talked to on my trip. Even before the review board published their report, one fellow told me he was sure the bridge could be built as designed. I asked him why, and he told me: 'Roebling says so.' Your father has quite a reputation."

"Yes, and I have a name to live up to. I wonder if they'll ever mean me when they talk about 'Roebling.'"

Warren stayed in New York long enough to help them move

John A. Roebling.

to the new house. The two men worked together, placing the furniture at Emily's direction, unpacking boxes and crates. Then Gouverneur left for Baltimore.

That night, after Johnny was asleep, Washington and Emily stood at the window of their bedroom and watched the ships on the river, their smokestacks just catching the last rays of the sun. The shadows cast by the boats worked magic on the water. It was blue, it was green, flecked with gold, streaked with silver, black, turquoise, purple. It moved and changed almost like a living thing, always reflecting the beauty and ugliness around it.

"You'll be able to watch the bridge go up from here, Em," said Washington. He picked up his old telescope, the one he had used as a scout in the war, and focused it on the river. "Yes, it's perfect. I can even see the men walking around on the boats."

"I really think that's what sold you on this house," Emily teased. "You couldn't bear to be away from the bridge—at least not out of sight of it."

"Maybe I couldn't bear to be away from you, did you think of that?"

"I like that idea better!"

"I don't suppose I'll see the bridge through this window very often, except by moonlight. You know I won't be home much once we get started, Em. Does it bother you?"

"Of course it does! But I should be used to the idea by now. If I get too lonely I'll just sit here in the window seat and look at you through the telescope."

The following months were busy ones, even though it was December before there were enough funds to think of buying materials. Washington and his father went over the plans again and again, surveyed every inch of ground on both sides of the river where the bridge approaches would be located, and took soundings of the river bottom to determine how deep the foundations would have to go.

Near the end of 1868 the newspapers reported that both New York and Brooklyn had subscribed to stock in the bridge. The municipality of Brooklyn had furnished three million dollars and New York half that amount. Combined with the money from private investors, this was enough to insure that the project would go ahead.

Washington wondered how Kingsley and his friends had persuaded the two cities to invest in the bridge, particularly when he read that Boss Tweed had purchased five hundred and sixty shares of his own. But the important thing was that the bridge corporation now had five million dollars in capital and could begin buying up land for the approaches.

The engineers worked through the rest of the winter and the spring completing their surveys. They hoped to start construction by midsummer. The last question to be solved was the exact location of the Brooklyn approach. There were several possibilities, and a change in the approach would also mean that the towers would have to be lined up differently.

It was June 28, 1869, and they had been taking final sightings for the Brooklyn tower for three days. They were working on the old Fulton Street ferryboat pier, and Washington noticed a boat approaching from the other side of the river.

John Roebling was sighting through a transit, oblivious to what was going on around him. Washington watched the ferryboat. It seemed to him that it had not slowed as much as usual. Then he noticed several of the crew members leaning over the rail, grinning. He remembered the black looks they had been getting from the boatmen all day—his father said they feared the new bridge would cost them their jobs.

Just before the ferry hit the pier, it dawned on Washington: they were going to give his father a jolt and throw off his calculations. There was a bump, and the screech of wood on wood. The transit jumped, and John Roebling doubled over, moaning. His right foot had been caught in a gap between the planks of the pier which had closed up when the ferry boat hit.

The gap opened again when the boat moved away after the impact, and Washington pulled the shoe and stocking off. His father's foot looked like a bloody piece of meat, with the toes so mangled it was impossible to tell one from another.

7 the bridge demands a life

With the help of a passer-by, Washington got his father into a hack and told the driver to take them to his house. He took off his shirt and wrapped it around the mangled foot to soak up the blood. When the cab pulled up in front of Washington's house on Hicks Street, he and the driver carried the injured man upstairs and put him in the spare bed.

John Roebling's face was drained of color, and there were flecks of blood on his beard from places where he had bitten his lower lip. But his jaw was set, and his eyes flashed determination not to let the pain get the best of him.

"I'll bring a doctor right away," Washington told him.

"I suppose you'd better," said his father, "the toes will have to come off. But after that I'll tell you how to take care of me. . . ."

"Father, we can't use hydropathy for a thing like this! Well, we'll talk about it later. Right now, I'd better go."

A few hours later a doctor amputated the damaged toes. John Roebling refused to have any sort of anesthetic and endured the operation by clenching his teeth on a clean rag. When it was over, he fell into a deep sleep.

"Is he going to be all right?" Emily asked Washington after the doctor had gone.

"Oh, I think so. I saw men recover from worse wounds than

that during the war. Of course, there's still a possibility of blood poisoning or lockjaw. But you know Father. I can't ever remember him being really sick; he just *won't*. Hydropathy and will power—those are his weapons against illness. I'm afraid we'll have to go along with his method of treatment for the next few weeks. . . ."

"What is this hydropathy?" asked Emily. "Has something to do with water, doesn't it?"

"Yes, hydropathic medicine is a system of water treatments. It really does work on some things—fevers, quite often, or muscle injuries. I don't think it'll help with an amputation, but it can't hurt, and I know Father will insist on it."

In the following days Washington took over at the bridge site while Emily nursed his father. She followed the elder Roebling's directions, soaking his bandages in cold water and then dousing the injured foot with hot water. She carried buckets of water up and down the stairs, slopping it through the house and mopping up afterwards until she told Washington she never wanted to see another drop.

"I know this is hard on you," Washington told her. "He's not a very good patient—in fact, the word 'patient' just wasn't designed for my father."

"It's a lot harder for him than it is for me," said Emily. "He doesn't know how to be sick. Strong men like that just can't stand to be helpless. I only hope he will be able to get around again before long."

"Yes, I guess I can understand how he feels. I've never been sick, either, and I know it would be hard for me to spend a week in bed. . . ."

Then one morning Washington brought John Roebling's breakfast on a tray. The injured man was awake, but he said nothing. His face was gray, and there were deep circles under his eyes. When Washington started to prop him up on his pillows, he noticed the muscles of his father's jaw working convulsively. John Roebling moaned, and his eyes rolled.

Washington stood frozen for a moment, then ran from the room and told Emily:

"Send for the doctor! It's lockjaw!"

A neighbor brought the doctor while they tried to make John Roebling more comfortable. After the examination, Washington spoke to the doctor in the hallway.

"It's lockjaw, isn't it?"

"Yes, I'm afraid so."

"I saw cases of it in the war, but I never knew of a man who recovered. Is there any hope?"

"I wouldn't count on it. We don't know what causes lockjaw—only that it strikes after a wound of some kind. And we don't know of any effective treatment for it. I can give him morphine for the pain. . . ."

"I'm sure he won't allow it. He doesn't believe in drugs that cloud the mind."

"The pain will be very severe."

As Washington had predicted, John Roebling refused to take any sort of drugs. The pain grew worse, and the muscular spasms moved from his jaws through other parts of his body. Washington and Emily stood helpless, applying the water treatments only because the sick man believed in them.

There were moments, between the waves of pain, when he was almost normal. His mind never stopped working, and in those moments he would talk to Washington about the bridge or about some other project he had in mind.

One morning he called Washington into the room and showed him a design for a machine to lift him up in bed.

"Don't you think this could be useful?" he asked his son. "Think how many invalids there are who can't sit up by themselves! I'd like to try this, maybe get a patent on it."

65

How strange, Washington thought, that a man's mind can go on functioning even when his body is being torn apart.

That afternoon the family minister, Rev. John Brown of St. Paul's Episcopal Church in Trenton, brought Washington's stepmother Lucy for a visit. John Roebling seemed happy to see them and talked quite a bit, asking about the factory and his family and employees in Trenton. When they left, he fell asleep. At six o'clock the next morning—July 22, 1869—he died.

Washington's reaction was one of disbelief. He did all that was expected of him, helping with preparations for the funeral, going through his father's personal belongings, preparing the obituary for the newspapers. Yet something deep within his mind would not accept the fact that his father was dead.

He knew that he had never loved his father in the conventional way. There had been too many separations, too many harsh words and too little companionship for that. But he did feel something for his father. It was an emotion almost deeper than love, warmer than respect—an irrational conviction that John Roebling was essential, that the world could not get along without him.

The night before the funeral Washington dreamed that he was standing on the bank of the Ohio River, admiring the Cincinnati-Covington bridge. Then he noticed a slight twitch, and one of the diagonal stays came loose from its position at the top of the tower. Then another stay came loose and another, until they were popping like violin strings that had been overtightened. There was nothing he could do. The bridge sagged and then tipped sharply as one of the main cables snapped. Bricks began tumbling from the towers. Strangely, he could hear nothing, nor could he move. The towers came apart the roadway hung at a crazy angle, and then the whole thing slipped silently beneath the surface of the river. There was not a ripple, and no sign remained that there had ever been a bridge there.

66

The Roebling house in Trenton was packed for the funeral. A train from New York had brought five carloads of friends, including most of the directors of the New York Bridge Company. Outside in the yard stood the employees of the wire rope factory with their families, listening to the service through the open windows.

Washington sat with his brothers and sisters, hearing only snatches of the tributes paid to John Roebling:

". . . a man with faith in his skill, with confidence that was not conceit, and a strong will . . ."

". . . above all, he was responsible and honest. He never started building until he made sure the plan was right in his mind . . ."

". . . manufactured an unknown article, wire rope, and created his own market for it, laying the foundation of one of the world's greatest industries . . ."

The next day the family lawyer read John Roebling's will, which divided an estate worth more than a million dollars among the widow, the seven children, and some special beneficiaries like Charles Swan. The wire rope business was left to the four sons. Washington was not surprised to hear that John Roebling had ordered the lawyer to deduct from each son's share the amount that had been spent on him in previous years. Those old ledgers would be used now! Even the long-ago train ride to Niagara Falls was recorded and would be charged against his inheritance. How typical of his father, he thought, to be so meticulous and yet somehow so lacking.

Among the personal belongings in the estate was a box filled with more than a thousand sheets of paper, each covered with John Roebling's careful handwriting—the "Theory of the Universe." Somehow the sight of the manuscript made Washington feel more genuine sadness than he had experienced before, even at the funeral. This was the product of his father's mind, the result of endless nights of thought and work, and now it was packed away in a box, and it would probably remain so. This is what death really means, he thought—perhaps more, but certainly this.

A few weeks later Washington was notified by the Board of Directors of the bridge corporation that he had been appointed to succeed his father as Chief Engineer. That night he lay awake, the plans rushing through his mind. He thought of an ancient superstition that he had read of while a student at Rensselaer. It had been believed that building a bridge violated nature in some way and that in order to appease the gods a human being had to be sacrificed every time a river was bridged. "The bridge demands a life"—that was the phrase they used. His father's life had already been sacrificed. Would that be enough, he wondered, or would more lives be required before the East River was conquered?

Washington spent the fall putting the plans in final shape, directing the purchase of machines and materials, and hiring workmen and engineering assistants—several of whom had been his classmates at Rensselaer.

He took the week of Christmas off and forced himself to stay away from the plans. Little John stared at the Christmas decorations with the wonder of a one-year-old, and Washington grieved again for the things his own father had missed. No matter what, he vowed, he would spend holidays at home.

On January 2, 1870, the construction began. Washington supervised the workmen who were demolishing old houses along the Brooklyn waterfront where the approach would be. His breath billowed out in a silvery cloud as he spoke, and the new snow squeaked under his shoes. Everything seemed new that morning: the snow, the year, the bridge.

In the following weeks the approach area was cleared and the rubbish carted away. At the same time work began on the caisson that would be used to construct the Brooklyn tower. The caisson was to be built at Greenpoint, a spot five miles up the river from the bridge site. But before much progress had been made on the Brooklyn caisson, Washington decided to make a trip to St. Louis. James Eads was already digging the foundation of his bridge, using a compressed air caisson, and Washington had to see it.

"But didn't you see some compressed air work going on in Europe?" Emily asked him.

"Yes, but not at the depth we'll have to work at. Eads' is almost a hundred feet under the river, and the strong currents of the Mississippi make it even harder. I understand the workers have had some trouble with the bends, too. I don't want to risk men's lives in a caisson without knowing everything I can about it."

"That's true," said Emily. "I wouldn't want *you* going down under the river, either, without knowing all you can find out."

James Eads did not seem overjoyed to see Washington, and the two men were uncomfortable with each other from the beginning. Washington got the impression that Eads suspected him of trying to steal designs—an attitude completely foreign to Washington's idea of the relationship between engineers. He had always felt that engineering grew as a science when men shared their ideas and experiences. So he had always been glad to show his designs to anyone who wanted to see them. Eads seemed to feel that he was in competition with other engineers and had to protect his ideas from them.

They got off to a bad start when Eads stated flatly: "An arch bridge is always superior to a suspension bridge, Roebling."

"What makes you think so?" asked Washington, trying to keep his temper.

"Suspension bridges are too flimsy. They can't be made as stiff as a good, solid arch. . . ."

"That used to be true, but we've developed methods of making suspension bridges as strong as any other type of bridge, or stronger."

"Can't be done. Of course, an arch bridge has to have more piers and doesn't give as much clearance above the river. The steamboat men are giving me a hard time about *that*. But I still say my bridge will outlast yours."

In spite of his disagreement with the man, Washington had to admire his knowledge and skill. He had designed a bridge that would withstand the gigantic Mississippi floods, the floating ice in winter, the windstorms, and tornadoes. He was not afraid to try new ideas and seemed to have the ability to make them work. Like Washington, he was planning to use steel in much of his structure, despite widespread suspicion of the new metal.

Grudgingly, Eads took Washington to the caisson. He showed him the plans as they stood on the deck but hesitated to let Washington go inside. The huge wooden box was already sunk deep beneath the river's sandy bottom, and full crews were working in it. Eads explained the mechanics of the system, the special pipe he had invented to expel sand and water from the bottom, and the pumps he used to keep the compressed air pressure at the right level inside.

"Has it been settling evenly as the men dig in the bottom?" Washington asked.

"Quite well, most of the time. Occasionally the 'shoe' at the base hits a boulder, and that has to be removed. But of course I've been very careful to distribute the weight properly on top of the caisson, so it will bear down evenly."

"Have you had trouble with caisson disease?"

Eads hesitated. "Bends? Well, . . . perhaps a little. Of course our men have had the usual symptoms of working under compressed air—tiring quickly, sweating, dizziness, and so forth. And

I'll admit a few of the men have been showing some more serious effects lately. Some complain of pain in the joints, and several have fainted when they came up. We've had to limit the working hours to four-hour shifts with eight hours rest between."

"Does that help?"

"I think so. We can't be sure. I've had my family doctor here, studying the problem, and he's hoping to have some answers soon. If only we knew what causes the disease! I don't want you repeating this, Roebling—the newspapers could blow it up into a major epidemic and we couldn't get laborers to work in the caisson."

"I won't say anything."

Just then the iron door on the top of the caisson clanged open, and workmen began climbing out at the end of one of the work shifts.

As the men walked past the two engineers, Washington studied them carefully. Most of them looked exhausted, particularly in view of the fact that they had only been working for four hours. Their faces were creased with black smudges from the candle smoke.

Then a slender, middle-aged workman stopped in his tracks. He looked almost surprised, as though someone had punched him in the stomach. He doubled over, clutching his knees, and fell to the ground. His incoherent moans reminded Washington of the wounded he had seen at Gettysburg—only this man had been struck by invisible bullets from an unknown enemy.

"Get Doctor Jaminet!" Eads shouted.

On the way back to New York Washington tried to concentrate on the things he had learned from James Eads and formulate his own plans for excavation. But always in the back of his mind was a picture of that laborer. European engineers had told Washington that the bends was painful, but he had not been prepared for the sight of an actual victim. He wondered how he could ask men to work for him and take such a risk. Yet there was no other way to sink the foundations deep enough.

Early on the morning of March 19, 1870, Washington stood in the Greenpoint construction yard, making a last-minute inspection of his caisson for the Brooklyn tower. It was made of timber, with the sides nine feet thick at the top tapering to an iron cutting edge or "shoe" at the bottom. Washington carefully checked all the seams, which had been filled with oakum, to be sure the caisson was airtight. He climbed a ladder to the top, or platform, and inspected the entrance shafts through which the men would go in and out, the supply shaft, the shaft for bringing up the dirt and rocks, and the pipe which would blow fine sand out and into the river. He examined the air pumps which would maintain the level of compressed air in the working chamber.

Sectional view of foundation showing caisson and mason work. The massive blocks of limestone and granite used in the masonry weighed from one and a half to six tons each. Over 3,000,000 feet board measure of yellow pine timber and about 35 miles of bolts were used in the construction of the caisson. The immense, bottomless wooden box covered a space of 102 by 168 feet, about three-eights of an acre of ground—nearly seven city lots.

Harper's Weekly Magazine, December 17, 1870

FOUNDATION LINE

Finally he climbed down and stood away from the great caisson, studying it to see if he could detect any flaw. It was decorated with colorful bunting, for today it would be launched and towed to the site of the Brooklyn tower. Then the actual building of the bridge could begin. As men dug the foundation in the bottom of the caisson, others would lay bricks on its roof so that the masonry towers of the bridge rose above the water at the same time that the caisson was sinking toward bedrock. Finally, when the tower had been completed and the foundation secured, the caisson would be filled with concrete.

The sun rose in the sky, and spectators arrived to watch the launching. A band lined up near the water's edge. The officials of the bridge corporation were there and some "city fathers" from both New York and Brooklyn. Washington saw Emily and little John on the edge of the crowd.

The caisson dwarfed the buildings around it and the ships in the harbor. The six tugboats that were waiting to tow it downriver looked like water bugs around a whale. Washington gave the signal, the blocks which had held it in place were removed, and the caisson slid down the ramp with a loud, grating noise.

It splashed into the water, and Washington knew that he was actually going to build the Brooklyn Bridge.

8 under the east river

It was time to go down. Washington stood on the deck of the caisson with Frank Farrington, his master mechanic, and a small crew. It was a sparkling May morning, and the air was fresh with the scent of last night's rain.

The past month had been spent in dredging ten thousand yards of mud out of the spot where the caisson would be sunk and in driving huge timber piles around it. The enclosure was complete now, the large boulders had been removed from the river bottom, and the caisson had been towed into position. Yesterday it had been sunk to the bottom, the water pumped out, and the working chamber filled with compressed air.

The top of the caisson still protruded above the water when its iron shoes were resting on the bottom. But even its three thousand tons of brick and timber did not prevent it from rising and falling with the East River tides, which could vary the height of the river as much as seven feet. Now it was low tide, and the caisson rested firmly against the bottom. Washington opened the round cover of the entrance shaft and climbed in, followed by Farrington and the workmen.

They descended an iron ladder into a small, bare compartment—the first air lock. Washington glanced up as the last man closed the shaft and saw the cover block out the sky like a cloud passing over the moon. He turned to Farrington and said as casually as he could: "Go ahead."

Farrington turned a valve, and compressed air began rushing into the chamber.

"Sounds like water," said one of the men. "Hope this thing ain't sprung a leak!" He pretended to be joking, but Washington noticed that the lighted candle in his hand was quivering slightly.

Another man clapped one hand over his ear. "Ow," he said, "that hurt!"

Washington's ears were popping, too, but not painfully. The feeling reminded him of traveling high in the Allegheny Mountains and of his balloon trips in the Civil War. He remembered a trick he had heard about from a French engineer.

"Hold your nose!" he told them. "You want to have equal pressure on both sides of your eardrums. They call it 'changing your ears.' Just hold your nose and blow until you can feel air in both ears." They did as he said and soon stopped complaining of pain in the ears.

By this time Farrington had removed a metal plate from the center of the floor, and stretching into the darkness below, they saw another iron ladder. Washington had been inside the caisson many times when it was being built; but now the dark passageway seemed as strange as a newly discovered cavern deep below the earth. He led the way down the ladder, his candle making a pitiful dent in the darkness.

It was hot in the shaft. Washington felt his pulse racing, and in a momentary spell of dizziness he hung on to the same rung of the ladder, until Farrington almost stepped on his fingers. Then he moved on. He did not know he had reached the bottom until he felt his foot sink ankle-deep in mud.

"I'm down," he called to the others, and was amazed at

the sound of his own voice. Usually a deep bass, he had become a tenor under compressed air! He laughed and again the sound was completely abnormal. The other men tried out their voices with similar results.

They waded through the slush of the river bottom, examining the working chamber by the inadequate light of the candles. There were fourteen sections in the working chamber, like large rooms. Washington explored them all, marking places where he thought more doors should be cut. The workmen, who would serve as foremen of the various crews in the caisson, followed and listened to his instructions. They tried sending a bucket of sand and rock up one of the excavation shafts, and it worked perfectly.

"We need to work out a system of communication with the engineers on top," Washington told the master mechanic. "It's a long way up, and it will get longer the deeper we go."

"Yes," Farrington agreed. "If something got stuck in one of the shafts, or the air pressure dropped suddenly, or we had a fire, we'd have to get word out in a hurry."

"Speaking of fire, that's another problem. We have to put some sort of lights down here, but fire will be a real danger. I can see that smoke will be annoying if we use candles. . . . "

Washington's falsetto voice trailed off. It was suddenly an impossible effort to speak. He felt weary, not with the good aching-muscle weariness of physical labor but with a new sensation, as though all the strength had been drained out of him. He looked at the others, and their faces showed similar exhaustion. According to his pocket watch, they had been in the caisson for nearly five hours.

"We'd better go up," he managed to say. "None of us is used to this compressed air yet, and I think we've had enough for today." They climbed back up the ladder, each step requiring a tremendous effort.

76

At home that night Washington told Emily about his exploration of the caisson. He tried to ignore the problems that were bothering him, but her persistent questions drew them all out: the mysterious bends, the danger of fire, the question of what to use for light, his uncertainty about safety precautions.

"It's like nothing else I've ever done," he told her. "Down there with all the water above you—it's like drowning in air. Only you don't drown, you just think you're going to."

"If it bothers you so much, do you have to keep going down? Couldn't your assistants supervise that part of it?"

"I can't ask men to risk their lives down there if I'm not willing to do it myself! Besides, it's not that I'm afraid. It's uncomfortable and I'd prefer working on the towers or cables in the open air, but nothing's going to happen to me. It's the others I'm thinking of."

Emily studied him curiously. "How do you know nothing's going to happen to you?" she asked.

"I'm strong and healthy," he said, "and I'm sure I can take it if anyone can." He could not tell her about his war experiences, how his fellow soldiers had been shot all around him and he had come through without a scratch. Yet he knew those battles had something to do with the way he felt now. Nothing would happen to him. He was sure of that.

As usual, Emily seemed to read his mind. "Just because you've never been seriously hurt before, you can't be sure you're safe forever," she said. "Think of your father. He was the same sort of man you are, and a petty little accident killed him."

"It's not like you to be so gloomy, Em," said Washington. "Building bridges is dangerous work; you've always known that. Worrying won't help."

"I'm sorry. I know it's silly. But I've been reading the articles about compressed air caissons in some of your engineer-

Harper's Weekly Magazine, December 17, 1870

Working beneath the shoe edge of the caisson.

ing journals. It sounds to me as if there is so little known about them, so many uncertainties. . . ."

"Your education is showing again." He laughed, trying to lighten her mood. "I'm beginning to see what Gouv warned me about. Reading my scientific journals, when you should have been peeling potatoes or something!" He lifted her off her feet and swung her around. "Back to the kitchen, Madam!"

The work started smoothly enough, with a total force of almost four hundred men working on the tower. In the underwater caisson, laborers—known as "sandhogs"—worked with picks and shovels, excavating the river bottom and sending the material up the shafts in great buckets. On top of the caisson other men laid bricks, while still others took care of the machinery.

There were problems before many weeks had passed. The candles which Washington installed for light in the caisson proved much too smoky, and he replaced them with calcium lights fed by compressed gas. On the top, workmen were bothered by occasional "blowouts." These happened when the shoe of the caisson caught on a boulder and left a gap through which compressed air could escape. Since the air pressure was

Harper's Weekly Magazine, December 17, 1870

Top: Air chamber through which the workmen entered and exited. *Bottom:* Sending up debris through the water shaft.

greater than that of the water, it sent a waterspout shooting up beside the caisson. Men on top had to dodge the mud, stones, and fish which the waterspout sprayed around them.

Washington spent more time in the caisson than any of the sandhogs. He quickly grew used to the effects of the compressed air and accepted its peculiarities as unthinkingly as he had the high altitudes on previous bridge towers.

Water and fine sand from the bottom of the caisson could be shot out into the river through pipes, but the larger rocks had to be transported out another way. At the bottom of each excavating shaft a large pit had been dug, which had been allowed to fill with water. The shaft was also partially filled with water, with an air lock at the top to prevent the compressed air from escaping through it.

Men carried the bulky material which they dug up to these pits in wheelbarrows and dumped it into the water. Then the bucket of a dredging machine was let down through the shaft. It reached under the water like a giant hand and grasped the rocks, lifting them up the shaft to the surface where other workmen hauled them away.

One afternoon shortly after the work began, a large stone became stuck below the water shaft where the dredge bucket could not reach it. The foreman came to Washington, who was in the caisson, and asked hesitantly what they should do about it.

"Someone will have to dive underwater with a crowbar and dislodge it," Washington told him.

"But, Sir, we were wondering—this compressed air is so strange, and no one has ever gone under the water in the caisson. Do you think it will have any effect?"

"Only one way to find out," said Washington, peeling off his coat. He left his outer clothing and shoes beside the pit and dove in, with a ring of sandhogs watching.

The water was warm on top because of the warm air in the caisson, but farther down it turned cold. He found the boulder and began to work at it, prying it up with a crowbar and pulling with his free hand. For a moment he thought he would not be able to get it loose. Then, just as his lungs began to burn and his throat to ache, he felt the rock give way and roll free. He floated to the top and surfaced, gasping. He was not prepared for the look of shock on the men's faces.

"What's the matter?" he panted.

"We thought you'd drowned for sure!" said the foreman. "You were under for nearly five minutes, Colonel Roebling! I checked it on my watch."

"Five minutes!" Washington pulled himself out of the pit and dried himself with a towel someone handed him. "I ran out of breath toward the end, but it wasn't any worse than many other dives I've made. And ordinarily I can stay under a minute and a half, two at most! It must be that the compressed air stays in your lungs longer. That's a good thing to know."

When the work had been going on for a month, Washington had a meeting with Charles Martin, his principal assistant, and the other engineers who were working on the bridge. The digging was going much too slowly, and something had to be done about it. Washington asked Frank Farrington to explain the difficulty.

"It's that hardpan," the master mechanic told them. "It doesn't come out well at all. The men break their pickaxes on it; the tools are wearing out at a fantastic rate. Even the teeth of the dredge buckets are wearing and breaking off."

"According to my figures," said Martin, "we've averaged only six inches a week. At that rate it would take us a year and a half to sink this caisson."

"Right," said Washington. "We're going to have to speed things up. I want to try blasting."

"In the caisson?" Martin asked. "Can we blast under compressed air?"

"That's what we're going to find out. It may work just as it does normally. Or—it might rupture eardrums or cause fires or blowouts—I'll admit those are possibilities. There has been some blasting in tunnels under compressed air, with no ill effects. But as far as I know, it hasn't been tried this deep under water."

"Won't we be taking quite a chance?" asked one of the assistants quietly.

"I intend to take the chance," Washington told him. "I'm

going to run some tests with explosions in the caisson—alone."

The others all began talking at once.

"You shouldn't take that risk alone!"

"You're the Chief Engineer! If anything happened to you—"

"Let me do it!"

Washington held up his hands until the men were quiet. Then he explained: "This is something I have to do, *because* I'm Chief Engineer. I have to know, from firsthand experience, how it will work. It's not that I wouldn't take your word for it, but it's my responsibility. If I start delegating this kind of job, I might as well go home and stick to paper work. I'm not that kind of engineer."

The next evening, after the last day shift had gone home, Washington went down into the caisson by himself. He had given the night crew—which usually did cleanup and repairs—the evening off. Over his shoulder he had a pack which contained pistols of various sizes, blasting powder, fuses, and matches.

There was no difference between night and day in the caisson. The calcium lights flickered against the walls, throwing weird shadows. Above ground it was unseasonably cool for late August, and he had needed his coat on the walk to the river. But here the temperature was always the same—seventy-eight. Beads of sweat formed on his skin as he walked through the caisson, and he mopped his face with a handkerchief.

The worst thing that could happen with blasting was a blowout of the water shaft. No one was sure how the force of an explosion would carry in compressed air, but the engineers feared that its effect might be heightened and might blow the doors from the air locks or force the water out of the excavation shaft. It this happened, the compressed air would escape, the caisson might be flooded, and anyone in it would probably lose his life.

Washington chose a compartment as far as possible from

the watershafts for his first experiment. He loaded the smallest of the pistols, and then paused. He wiped his hands and face, which were streaming with sweat again. Remembering how Emily had looked at him when he had gone out the door tonight, how Charles Martin had squeezed his hand when he had entered the caisson (Martin had insisted on waiting on the deck), he wondered why he was not more nervous than he was. "Cold-blooded," his fellow-soldiers had called him. He supposed he was.

"*Pop!*" The gun fired, its report sounding as muffled as though it had been shot off in another room. Except for the distortion of sound, Washington could discover no unusual results. His ears were unaffected; he checked the doors and shafts and could find nothing wrong.

He shot off the other pistols in various parts of the caisson. Then he planted a small charge of blasting powder in some boulders which the workmen had been breaking up. He attached a fuse, lit it, went into another compartment and lay down with his arms over his head. He heard the explosion, like a dull thud, and the sound of flying rocks hitting the walls of the compartment. Then nothing.

He found that the blasting powder had done its work, breaking up the boulders into easily disposable pieces. Since it was impossible to smell anything under compressed air, the odor of the blasting powder was no problem. As far as Washington could determine, the worst thing they would have to contend with would be smoke. The compartment where he had set off the blast was swirling with it. The thick black cloud obscured the lights and burned in his throat. They would have to be careful, too, to watch for fire after a blast—particularly since no one in the caisson could smell.

Washington set off progressively larger blasts throughout the working chamber and inspected the results until he was satisfied that it was safe to use explosives in the caisson. When he came out of the air lock, the stars were fading and there was a hint of dawn in the east.

Charles Martin was waiting for him. "How did it go?" he asked.

"Quite well, I think. Come on into the dressing room with me, and I'll tell you about it." Washington led the way to the shack beside the caisson which the men used for eating lunch, dressing, and cleaning up. Washington leaned over the sink to wash his face and hands and could hardly recognize himself in the mirror.

"It's a good thing my little boy isn't here," he said to Martin. "He'd think I'm the Bogeyman for sure!" Washington's face, hair, and beard were black from the smoke, except for streaks which had been traced by sweat. His eyes were bloodshot, his clothes disheveled. "Anyway," he went on, "in spite of the way I look, the experiment was a complete success. Let me tell you about it. . . . "

After they began blasting through the hardpan, the work went much faster. The caisson lowered from twelve to eighteen inches each week, with crews firing as many as twenty blasts in a single watch. At the same time, bricklayers on top of the caisson were building up the tower. By late fall the outline of the Brooklyn tower was a definite landmark on the skyline.

One Sunday morning Washington woke early. He did not need to get up, for he had always given his men Sundays off and there would be no work done on the bridge today. But for some reason he could not get back to sleep. He climbed out of bed as quietly as he could, so as not to disturb Emily, and tiptoed to the window.

He liked to look at the tower at this time of day, when the sun's rays first reached it. He picked up his telescope and focused it on the deck of the caisson. The watchman sat dozing in a chair beside the lock of one of the water shafts. His two helpers were talking on the other side of the caisson. Everything was as it should be.

Suddenly a torrent of water burst out of the caisson with a deafening roar. As Washington watched, the column rose five hundred feet in the air, scattering stones and yellow mud everywhere. He could not see what had happened to the men who had been on the caisson.

"What is it?" Emily asked, sitting up in bed.

"A blowout!" Washington was already pulling on his clothes. "One of the main water shafts. I've got to get down there!"

9 the big blowout

When Washington got to the Fulton Street corner he had to move against a crowd of people running away from the waterfront. The street was slippery with mud, which had rained down for blocks around.

"A ship exploded in the river!" someone shouted, and Washington heard the tale being repeated as he hurried toward the river. There was no use stopping to explain; the truth would be known soon enough.

There was another crowd at the river trying to find out what had happened. Washington pushed through them and climbed onto the caisson, which was covered with a layer of yellow mud and stones.

At first he thought there was no one left on the deck. Then he noticed a pile of coal moving, and from it emerged one of the workmen, sooty and terrified.

"Colonel!" he shouted when he recognized Washington. "I thought the whole thing had blown up! You should've seen the water. . . . "

"I know," said Washington. "One of the shafts blew out. Where are the other men?"

"I was with George when it happened. He dove right off into the river. But I can't swim a stroke, so I hid under the coal pile. . . . "

"What about the watchman?"

"I didn't see what happened to him."

They hurried to the side of the caisson and saw a man pulling himself out of the water and climbing up the side of the caisson. He seemed unhurt. Washington sent the two of them to the dressing shack to change clothes and clean up.

He found the watchman lying near a stack of bricks. The man's forehead was bleeding, and he was unconscious. Washington revived him by splashing water on his face.

"Ooooooh," he moaned, "what happened?"

"A blowout. One of the main water shafts. You must have been hit by a rock. How do you feel?"

"Like the whole tower fell on me! A water shaft, you say? Oh, my head!"

"You'd better go and lie down in the shack. Tell one of the other men to get Doctor Smith."

Now Washington had to find out what had happened. He could see by the debris around it that the south water shaft had blown out. Nearby, the doors to the main air lock had fallen open when the escape of the compressed air had released the pressure on them. He had only to look down to learn whether the caisson had flooded. . . .

"I came as soon as I realized what happened." Charles Martin came running up behind Washington. "Was anyone hurt?"

"Not seriously, I think. Thank goodness this happened on Sunday and not when we had a full crew below! Come on, let's take a look." Washington led the way through the rubbish to the air lock.

They could see all the way to the dry river bottom. Not a drop of water had leaked into the caisson after the blowout.

"I can hardly believe it," said Martin. "We did our best to make the caisson watertight, but without the pressure of the compressed air. . . "

"We're lucky the caisson had already been sunk well into the mud and hardpan, so nothing could get in around the bottom. If this had happened three months ago, it would have flooded for sure. Well, we'd better bring the pressure up again."

They closed the air lock, replaced the water in the blown-out shaft, and started the air pumps. Within an hour the gauges showed that the pressure in the caisson was twenty pounds per square inch, the current working level. Washington and Charles Martin went below to see what the blowout had done to the working chamber.

The caisson had acted like a balloon with the air suddenly released; it had been driven down into the river bed with tremendous force. They found it had settled ten inches in some places. Where it had run against large boulders, the shoe had been badly twisted, but on the whole the damage was not too severe. When they came to the south water shaft, they saw what had caused the blowout.

"The dam must have washed away!" said Martin.

Washington nodded. "The watchman had orders to check it every two hours through the night. My guess is, he fell asleep and didn't go down."

"We're lucky the caisson wasn't hurt any worse than it was."

"Yes—and if this happens again before we're done, we might not be so fortunate. I think I'm going to have the men build a brick pier down here, to support the roof while we finish up. We only have a few more feet to go. I don't want another blowout to ruin the whole structure this close to the end."

When Washington went home that night, he felt oddly relieved. They had dreaded the possibility of a bad blowout since the compressed air work had begun. Now it had happened, and the caisson had survived it. No one had been badly hurt or killed.

December 1870: Work in progress on the Brooklyn pier a year after construction was begun.

He decided to stop work early the next evening and take Emily out to dinner. He had been neglecting her lately. The day was spent cleaning up after the blowout, and by six the job was done well enough so that Washington could leave. A neighbor came in to take care of Johnny, and they took a cab to Delmonico's restaurant.

Washington had bought a newspaper to read on the way. He glanced through several stories about the political situation in New York following the recent fall of Boss Tweed, former leader of Tammany Hall. Since Tweed had been defeated in the fall election there were rumors that he would be arrested any day and tried for his misuse of city funds. Then Washington saw the story on the blowout at the bridge, and his happy mood dissolved.

September 1872: The Brooklyn pier is completed to the roadway.

Early Sunday morning Brooklyn was showered with mud and rocks as a waterspout at the site of the bridge under construction exploded like a volcano. Three workmen on the caisson escaped with minor injuries.

A prominent Brooklyn businessman and civic leader echoed the thoughts of many others when he asked: ' How long is our city to be subjected to the dangers of this unknown, untried method of excavation? Why do we need a bridge at all? Or, if we must have one, why not one constructed by conventional methods? Must we wait until real tragedy strikes before putting a stop to this project?'

"I'll bet the man who wrote this story made up that quotation just to stir up interest!" Washington said angrily. He read the story to Emily.

"Well," she said, "that's nothing new. They've been calling the bridge 'unsafe' all along. I don't think people will pay much attention to this, do you?"

"I don't know. Let's forget about it." Washington put the paper away, determined not to spoil the evening.

It was good to enjoy the soft lights, the music, the colors of the draperies, and the women's gowns. Washington told himself that he had spent too much time in the underworld of the caisson. He had forgotten how pleasant it was to savor roast duck slowly, listening to Emily's soft voice instead of the falsetto shrieks of the men in the working chamber.

"Aren't you John Roebling, the engineer?"

A tall, olive-skinned young man intruded, pulling up a chair without any invitation and smiling confidently.

"My father was John Roebling," Washington told him, trying not to sound annoyed.

"Oh, yes, my error, your name is. . . Lincoln? No, Jefferson?"

"Washington Roebling. And you?" His voice was quite

cold now, and he gripped his knife and fork more tightly than necessary.

"Oh, you wouldn't know me. I'm just a reporter, I work for the *Herald Tribune.* I'd like to ask you a few questions."

"My wife and I are having dinner. . . . "

"It'll only take a minute," said the reporter smoothly, ignoring Washington's protest. "Tell me, do you think the East River Bridge will ever be finished?"

"Will you leave our table, or shall I call the manager?"

"I suppose that was a bit impertinent. Well, another question. I have it on good authority that the investigation of Boss Tweed's affairs will reveal quite a scandal in the use of the bridge funds. Would you like to comment on that possibility?

"No, I wouldn't."

"What about that waterspout yesterday? Isn't it true that the construction site is a menace, and it's only a matter of time until someone is killed?"

Washington stood up, almost overturning his chair, and beckoned to a waiter. The reporter gave it up then. He rose, bowed gracefully to Emily, and strolled away with a last insolent smile at Washington.

The evening was spoiled. There was nothing left but to pay the bill and go home. Washington was grateful that Emily did not try to restore their gaiety, or to make light of the encounter. He was in no mood to talk about it.

One night, early in December, Washington was preparing to go home when a foreman came running after him, calling out a word he had dreaded for over a year:

"Fire! Fire in the caisson!"

The scene in the working chamber made Washington think of a book he had studied in school years before: Dante's *Inferno.* The men of the night crew were milling around in a panic, some carrying buckets of water, others struggling with a high-pressure hose which they had not been able to turn on. Smoke swirled about them, and above all the other noise was the ominous crackling sound of fire.

"It's in the ceiling over here," the foreman shouted, leading Washington through several compartments. "I think one of the men must have held a candle too close. . . . "

The blaze had a good start; Washington's heart sank when he saw it eating a large hole in the timbers of the roof. "Get that high-pressure hose in here," he called out. Then he drew the foreman aside. "Send most of your crew home. We can work better with just a few in here. Ask about a dozen men to stay— the most dependable ones."

They got the hose turned on the blaze, and as it wriggled like a snake in their arms, the room echoed with the hiss of scalding steam. By this time the fire had spread down the walls and into other chambers. Washington and his crew staggered from room to room, following the fingers of flame.

Shortly after midnight they had the worst of it under control. Some of the assistant engineers had heard of the fire and had come to help, so Washington was able to send the rest of the sandhogs home. With Martin, Farrington, and the others he searched the caisson, drenching it with water from the hoses, feeling along the walls for heat. At last they came back to the chamber where the fire had started.

Washington stared at the charred roof, his body suddenly limp with the weakness brought on by exertion and the compressed air. He coughed, his smoke-filled lungs aching.

"Colonel Roebling," said Farrington, "hadn't you better get some rest? It's five o'clock in the morning. You must have been down here for at least seven hours—and at this depth we don't let anyone work more than four."

"I'm all right. We're going to have to find out how far the fire went into the roof. There's fifteen feet of solid timber up there, and for all we know a fire might be blazing away out of sight. If there is, and we don't get it, the whole caisson could be destroyed and the tower would collapse."

"We'd better start taking borings," said Martin. "How deep should we go?"

"We can't take any chances. Go in at least five feet." Washington studied the blackened ceiling as several of his assistants went after tools. It began to move slowly, like a dark rain cloud being blown by the wind. He wondered for a moment whether the fire had already gone through the roof, and the whole tower was crashing down. Then he stopped seeing and thinking.

He opened his eyes in the dressing shack. He was lying on one of the beds they kept there for men who became sick on the job. Above him floated the anxious faces of Martin, Farrington, Doctor Smith—and Emily.

"What happened?" he asked. His voice sounded detached, as though someone else had spoken.

"You collapsed in the caisson," the doctor told him. "You've been unconscious for nearly an hour. How do you feel?"

Washington's arms and legs felt like iron bars. Tiny, stabbing pains moved through him like a swarm of bees. But his mind had cleared, and he was sure he could pull himself together.

"I'm all right," he said finally. "Just exhausted, I guess. What about the fire?"

"We thought we had it out," Martin told him. "Borings at two and three feet showed nothing. But then, at four feet—well, that fourth course of timber is a mass of live coals."

"We'll have to flood the caisson," Washington decided. He started to get up, but his head throbbed violently and he sank back on the bed. Emily sat beside him and put her cool hand on his forehead. "How did you get here?" he asked her.

94

"One of the engineers came and said you'd collapsed. They thought then it might be the bends. You've got to rest for a while, Wash—don't try to go back down there."

"Your wife is right," said Doctor Smith. I insist that you have absolute quiet and rest for a few hours before you leave here. We don't know what happened to you in the caisson; but even if it is simple exhaustion you're in no shape to resume work."

Washington agreed to rest for an hour or two while his assistants arranged to have the caisson flooded. He soon felt much better, and by ten o'clock in the morning he was back on the deck of the caisson. Thirty-eight streams of water were being poured into the working chamber from above. City fire engines were lined up at the water's edge, with the harbor fire boat *Fuller,* a Navy tug, and another boat adding their hoses. By midafternoon the chamber was full, and Washington decided to leave it that way for several days to make absolutely sure that the fire was out. He went home.

It was not until he got back to the house and had a light supper that he realized how tired he was. This time he felt not the weakness brought on by compressed air but complete mental and physical weariness. He carried the strain and sleeplessness of the past hours in every bone and muscle.

"You ought to go to bed," Emily told him softly.

"Now? It's only seven!"

"I can tell by looking at you that you need sleep. And since you're going to leave the caisson flooded for a few days, I hope you'll use them to get completely rested. Do you know how frightened I was when they came and told me you'd been brought up unconscious? Don't let it happen again!"

"Maybe you're right. I guess I am a little tired. I'll take it easy tomorrow, anyway—spend some time with you and Johnny."

Washington slept the clock around that night and took another long nap the following afternoon. He played with his son, talked with Emily, even got out the violin he had not touched for years. When the time came to go back to the bridge, he felt like a new person.

It took six hours to force all the water out of the caisson. Washington stood on the deck as the air pumps worked. A cold rain was falling, and he thought of the faraway spring when both towers would be finished. Then he could do the work he liked best—the good outdoor labor of cable stringing and painting.

When the water was out, they went below to inspect the caisson. It had not been damaged by the flooding—in fact, the timbers had swollen until they were tighter than before. Then began the work of repairing the effects of the fire.

At first they tried simply filling the burned parts of the roof with cement. But then they found that there was a layer of soft charcoal around the cement. Washington refused to take chances on the strength of his tower; he ordered all the cement removed. Then a crew of carpenters crawled into the cavities and scraped off all the charcoal by hand. Following his rule not to ask his workmen to do a job he wouldn't do himself, Washington helped with this.

It took two months. They crawled into the holes of the roof like termites and lay in impossible positions, breathing dust and smoke. When Washington came up from one of these sessions he was black all over; he even spit a black stream from the coal dust in his lungs.

At last the holes were "clean" and could be refilled with concrete. When the job was done, the foundation was as strong as it had ever been—perhaps even stronger. There were eleven feet of solid timber that had never been touched by the fire, and the burned parts had been completely repaired. Yet newspaper critics harped on the effects of the fire, implying that the Brooklyn tower would be standing on a few half-burned pieces of wood.

The Brooklyn caisson reached its final position at the end of 1871. The cutting edge was forty-four feet below high tide on the East River. The sandhogs began filling the working chamber with concrete, layer by layer.

It was the day after Christmas. Washington was working in the chamber, and he was pleased with the rate of progress. The caisson would be filled in a month or two, and then they could begin the work on the New York side.

He moved to one of the far compartments of the caisson, where the concrete was being mixed. They had to mix it below now, because it was too cold on the deck. He had not quite reached the mixing room when he became aware of a peculiar, hissing noise.

Then there was a roar; the lights went out, and water began seeping into the caisson.

10 the bends

Washington's mind worked quickly as he felt his way along the wall of the caisson. The roaring noise had to mean another blowout. This time a full crew of men was trapped in the caisson! They faced two dangers: the rising water and the sudden change in air pressure.

He slogged through the water to the center of the caisson, where most of the men had been working. They were in a state of complete confusion—shouting, calling for help, bumping into each other, and stumbling over equipment.

"Which shaft blew out?" Washington asked, but no one seemed to know. Recognizing his voice, they swarmed around him.

"Colonel Roebling! Get us out of here!"

"We'll drown!"

"The air's gone. . . . "

Washington did his best to calm the sandhogs and questioned them until he learned that the noise had been loudest near one of the two supply shafts. He found a candle in a box near the entrance, lighted it, and used it to find his way to the supply shaft. By this time the icy water was up to his knees. He held the flickering candle under the shaft and saw that both doors hung open.

Around the bottom of the shaft was a pile of broken stones and gravel which had jammed the lower door open.

"Find shovels," Washington told the men. "We've got to clear the shaft and get the door closed." He did not wait for the shovels but began digging at the pile with his bare hands.

In a few minutes they had the gravel cleared away and were able to push the door shut. Then Washington led them to the main shaft and told them to climb up, go through the air lock and out as usual. "Don't hurry," he said, "and rest in the dressing shack when you go out."

He stayed below, searching through the caisson to be sure everyone was out. The water had stopped rising when he closed the supply shaft door, but in some places it was almost waist-high. The mud sucked at his shoes, and the drop in air pressure was beginning to make him feel dizzy. His candle made little light in the fog that swirled around the working chamber. He found no one.

When Washington climbed out of the caisson, he met Charles Martin, just preparing to come down after him.

"We thought something had happened to you," said Martin. "What caused the blowout?"

"It looked to me as if an extra load of gravel was dumped in the supply shaft by mistake. The weight of it overcame the air pressure and forced the lower door open. Then, of course, the air escaped."

They went into the dressing shack, and the sandhogs who were resting there cheered when they saw Washington. He looked at them blankly. "You should have heard them tell about what happened below," Martin whispered. "To them you're a hero—saved them all from certain death."

"All I did was give them some direction. I learned something down there, Charles. All the safety measures in the world

Colonel Washington A. Roebling.

are useless if the men panic. They had only to shut the shaft and climb out—but there's something about that caisson that frightens them. The same men working above ground would probably have handled an even worse situation quite calmly."

"The panic didn't seem to affect you," Martin said. "They think you're absolutely fearless."

On the way home, Washington wondered again about his reputation for bravery. Why was it that he never seemed to be afraid when others were? Was it because he had never suffered a real injury, in spite of all the dangers he had lived with?

He talked about it with Emily that night, and her comment surprised him.

"It's your lack of fear that worries me," she said. "Don't you realize that fear is a good thing? You seem to think nothing bad can happen to you! So you take foolish chances, and everyone thinks you're brave. Some day your luck is going to run out, and I wonder how brave you'll be then!"

Washington was startled not only by what she said but by the force of her anger. Emily's temper did not flare often, and he had thought that she understood his commitment to the bridge. Now her outburst wounded him. He had been rather proud of the men's praise, and her criticism seemed unfair.

"We're doing something new that's never been done before," he told her. "I have to lead every step of the way, be sure it's done right. This bridge is my responsibility, and so are the lives of the men who work on it. . . . "

"And so is your own life! Did you ever think of that? How much good will you do the bridge or the workmen or anyone, if you throw your own life away?"

"That's enough, Emily! I'll decide what risks I have to take in my work, and I don't want you interfering!"

Washington walked around Brooklyn that night, hurt and bewildered. He had been sure that in Emily he had found a wife who would share his life fully and would understand the requirements of his job and his own dedication to it. Instead, she was nagging him like any other woman! Was this why his father had spent so little time at home?

In the following weeks they lived together under a sort of truce—polite and even pleasant to each other but always with the unspoken, unfinished argument between them.

By May, 1871, the Brooklyn caisson had been filled with concrete, and on that solid foundation the tower rose seventy-five feet above the river. The masons had only to lay another twenty feet of bricks to complete the Brooklyn tower. It was time to move to the New York side.

There would be more problems on this tower. Borings showed that they would have to go almost twice as deep to reach bedrock—through layers of quicksand. Eighty feet below the surface of the river they would have to dig a base for the tower that would cover an area as large as seven city lots when finished.

But Washington and his staff had also learned a great deal from their work on the Brooklyn tower. He had the second caisson lined with a thin layer of boiler iron to prevent a recurrence of fire. A system of double air locks was installed to permit more men to move in and out of the working chamber. Since there would be a longer climb, a spiral staircase was used in place of the ladder to help ease fatigue. The air locks were moved to the bottom of the entrance shaft so the men would not have to climb in compressed air. The walls were whitewashed to give better reflection of light, and sixty double gas burners illumined the working chamber.

By November the weight of the masonry was sufficient to keep the caisson from rising at high tide, and the excavation began. A large pile dock had been built nearby for the offices, sheds, dressing rooms, and equipment. Conscious of the increased threat of the bends, Washington had added a small infirmary as well and had hired Doctor Smith to keep regular hours there.

The sandhogs were a mixed crew—Germans, Irish, Scottish, and Americans of many national backgrounds. Washington liked to dig beside them, listen to their talk, and joke with them. He grew to have an enormous respect for these laborers who risked their lives for a dollar seventy-five a day.

One day in January Washington was wielding a shovel in the muck of the East River bottom with the afternoon shift of workmen. This particular part of the river had been used as a dump ground for years, and the digging was unpleasant.

"I thought this compressed air was supposed to put your nose to sleep," said one of the sandhogs with a grimace.

"This garbage'd stink up an acre of roses," said another

man. "Look at that dead cat—I think I'm goin' to lose me lunch."

"I never knew you Irishmen were so delicate." A German sandhog laughed. "After that corned beef and cabbage you eat, Patrick, I'd think you could stand anything!"

Pat McKay, the Irishman, tossed a decaying fish at the German. "Here, this smells about like that sausage you had yesterday!"

"Let's just get this garbage out of here as fast as we can," said Washington lightly, stepping in before a battle broke out between the Germans and the Irish. "If we start throwing it around, we'll all come up reeking!"

"The Colonel's right." McKay chuckled. "My wife ain't too eager to let me in the house at night as it is!"

Just then a bell was rung, signifying the end of the shift. The men put their tools away and filed into the first air lock when the door was opened. Washington saw to it that they all sat quietly for a few moments, holding their noses and blowing to "change their ears." They moved into the next air lock and repeated the procedure, then climbed the long spiral to the top of the caisson. Coming out into the sunlight, Washington turned to Pat McKay and said, "Good to get a whiff of that fresh air, isn't it?"

The Irishman started to answer, then stiffened. His florid face went gray, and he clutched at his thighs.

"What's wrong?" Washington asked sharply.

"Oh . . . nothin', I guess. Just a funny feeling for a minute and a pain in the leg. It's gone now."

"Get over to the infirmary right away and have the doctor examine you. And I want you to stay there and rest for at least two hours."

Watching McKay move slowly toward the infirmary, Washington felt apprehensive. The caisson was as deep now as the

Brooklyn caisson had been in its final position, and they still had a long way to go. Was this the beginning of an epidemic of bends, as the air pressure increased?

Later in the day Doctor Smith confirmed that Pat McKay had suffered a mild attack of caisson disease. "I told him to take a few days off, rest up," said Smith. "But I think he'll be fine."

"What worries me is the possibility of more cases, worse ones," said Washington.

"There can be. We know so little about the disease. I understand there have been several deaths among the workmen on the St. Louis bridge. Is there any chance of getting some advice from Eads?"

"No," Washington said flatly. He had gone all the way to St. Louis to ask for help once, and James Eads had greeted him with suspicion. Then several months ago Eads had published an article accusing Washington of stealing his caisson design from the Mississippi bridge! There were some similarities but also many differences between the two caissons. Washington's designs were his own. He was willing to admit that he had learned from other engineers. But to accuse him of stealing . . . ! They would have to deal with the bends as best they could; he would not ask Eads for help.

As spring came on, there were more attacks. The first ones were mild, but gradually they became more severe. Several men were temporarily paralyzed. Eventually all of them returned to work, and not one suffered any permanent damage.

Doctor Smith and Washington worked out a list of health rules which they hoped would help offset the effects of the compressed air. The shifts were cut to two hours at a time, twice a day. Men with any sign of weak hearts or lungs were not allowed to go down.

Still, the strain and fear began to tell on the sandhogs. Newspapers trumpeted the reports of bends. Laborers began to quit as they saw friends struck down by the strange malady. Nearly every day a new man came on the job.

One morning late in April Washington hired a German named John Meyers to fill a vacancy in the excavation crew. Meyers was a short, heavy man about forty years old. Washington talked with him in German for a few minutes, had Dr. Smith examine him thoroughly, and then sent him down to dig with the morning shift.

Two hours later the men came up, and Washington happened to be standing near the shaft checking an engine. He noticed that Meyers, the new man, did not go into the dressing shack with the others. Instead, he sank down with his back against the wall and his head between his knees. Washington hurried over to him and asked if he was sick.

"I don't know," Meyers replied weakly. "I don't feel just right. . . . "

"You'd better go over to the infirmary," Washington told him.

"No, I'm not that bad off. I think if I could go home and rest for a while, I'd be fine. I live in a boarding house just a block from here."

"All right, but I'm going to send one of the men with you to be sure you get home all right."

Washington watched the two men go and then forgot the incident, as he became absorbed in his work. But less than half an hour later the man he had sent with Meyers came running back, a look of terror on his face.

"It's Meyers, Colonel. He's . . . he's dead!"

"Dead? What happened?"

"When we got inside the boarding house, he told me he had a terrible pain in the stomach. At the top of the stairs he fell down and passed out. And before we could get him into bed—he died!"

Just a week later Patrick McKay was carried out of the caisson, unconscious. Doctor Smith had him moved at once to the large Park Hospital, and Washington went there to see him.

McKay was in a coma, his face pale and his lips blue. The nurses said he had come to once and begged pitifully for water. By nightfall he, too, was dead.

A little more than two weeks after that, in mid-May, there was a third death. The victim this time was an Englishman, William Reardon. The papers that carried news of this death were also full of angry protest and demands for protection of the sandhogs. Several editorials seemed to imply that the instances of caisson disease were caused by negligence on the part of the bridge officials.

"As though I wouldn't do anything I could to prevent it," Washington fumed to Emily. "If we only knew the cause! Why do some get it and not others? Why do some die and some get only mild cases? I *know* this method of excavation is a good one, and we've learned so much already. We've got to find out how to stop the bends, too!"

"You know what frightens me. I keep wondering when it will be your turn," said Emily.

"I'll be all right. It seems to be older men or those with weak constitutions who suffer most. I've never been sick in my life! Anyway, we have to keep trying. If people hadn't been willing to experiment, we'd still be swinging over rivers on twisted vines!"

Washington spent more and more time below, watching for the slightest clue to the mystery. Several times he experienced mild cramps or dizzy spells, but he told no one. He was sure that these minor symptoms were his dose of the bends; that because of his youth and strength this was all that the compressed air could do to him.

In June he was asked to appear before the executive committee of the bridge corporation and explain why his expenses were running above the original estimates. He listed the added costs in detail: the fire, the improvements in the design for safety reasons, the cost of labor, the wider roadway, and the high span. Then he informed them that the bridge might cost close to ten million dollars, instead of the seven million John Roebling had originally estimated.

Washington was pleasantly surprised at the sympathetic attitude of most of the board members. They seemed to understand his problems and to be confident that the additional funds could be raised. It was a relief to leave the financial problems to them and be able to concentrate on construction again.

The next morning on his walk to the river Washington was aware of the beauty around him for the first time in weeks. He had been so busy preparing his report that he had not even noticed the full blossoming of spring in New York. It was one of those June days that seem to shimmer with color and light— clear, warm, with just a hint of a breeze.

He stepped into the shaft reluctantly, taking a last look at the brightness above. Then the hot, stale air enveloped him, and the sun was gone.

Washington worked through the morning shift and was about to go out with the men when he noticed a boulder jammed under one of the walls.

"This will have to come out," he told the foreman. "It looks like a bad one. I'll work at it while the shifts change."

They were digging through quicksand now, which at one moment could be packed hard as cement and again could yield like pudding. The boulder was wedged into a hard layer of the quicksand, but Washington thought he detected a shifting pool just below. It would be tricky to blast out the boulder without sending the caisson tilting into a soft spot.

The boulder was finally removed with picks and crowbars.

Washington looked at his pocket watch and saw that it was three o'clock. He had not meant to stay down so long—it had been almost five hours. He started for the air lock.

As he reached for the door, a sudden pain ripped through his stomach. He bent over, moaning in agony, as it moved into his legs. He felt as though the flesh were being torn from his bones. Then the darkness closed around him.

11 the prisoner

The pain had not gone away when he regained consciousness. He knew he was in the little infirmary on the pier and that the doctor was bending over him, but his mind was blurred by the agony in his muscles.

"Can you hear me?" Doctor Smith was asking. As Washington watched, unable to answer, the doctor's face split and became two identical images, floating before his eyes like twins.

Washington tried desperately to speak. His mouth was dry, and his throat ached. His tongue and lips refused to form words; all he could manage was a moan.

"We'll have to get him to Park Hospital at once," Doctor Smith said to someone. "It's bad—very bad. I don't know if he'll last more than a few hours."

Time and place had no meaning any more. He seemed to be drifting in and out of his body; sometimes with almost normal perceptions and incredible pain, other times in a sort of numb suspension. He thought he saw Emily, but it was as though she were on the other side of a glass wall and he could not reach her. The doctor was there, and strangers, and once he was sure his father's face floated past him.

In one of his most lucid moments he heard someone say that he would certainly be dead by morning. Then he knew that the release for which his body longed was his enemy. He felt himself sinking back into oblivion, the pain fading, and he forced himself to struggle. His mind seized on one thought and held it: as long as he was in pain, he was alive.

Then finally his vision cleared, and he lost the sensation of wrestling with death itself. He even answered a few of the doctor's questions, though speech was unbelievably difficult for him.

"Where is the pain centered now?"

"My . . . legs . . . "

"The abdominal pains are gone?"

"Better . . . "

"You have double vision?"

"Not . . . now . . . "

"I think the worst is over," said Smith. "The attack seems to be subsiding. I never believed you'd survive it. You'd better get some rest now; it's been a long night. I'll give you some morphine to help you sleep."

When he woke again, Emily was there. He tried to speak, but she shook her head and put a hand over his lips.

"Doctor Smith says you're not to talk. It's too much of an effort. But he thinks you're out of danger now. With plenty of rest and quiet you should be able to go home in a few days."

Washington wanted to ask when he could go back to the bridge. He decided that they probably would not know, anyway, until he had recovered from the effects of the attack. Some workmen had been away from the job as much as three weeks after having the bends; he would have to be patient.

His legs were aching, and he thought a change of position might help. Then he realized that he could not move them.

"Am I . . . strapped down?" he croaked.

"Shhhh! No, I don't think so."

"Can't . . . move . . . legs."

For an instant she could not hide her fear. Then she composed her face and said softly, "You're just exhausted. I think Doctor Smith said there's often a sort of temporary paralysis after these attacks. I'd better go now and let you rest."

A week later, when Washington was taken home, he still could not move the lower part of his body. The only sensation he felt was pain, a constant ebb and flow which traveled through all his limbs but was centered in his useless legs. The doctor kept reassuring him that temporary paralysis was common, but as the days passed without improvement, Washington sensed that even he was losing hope.

The attack had left his nerves exquisitely sensitive. He could not bear any sort of noise or confusion in the room, so he could only see little John for a few minutes at a time. Even Emily's soft voice often struck him like chalk being squeaked across a blackboard. The simplest conversation left him utterly drained; loud noises were torture.

Yet his inner self, his mind and personality, seemed to be unchanged by the physical torment. He was like a stranger in his own body; a prisoner, trapped and clamoring for freedom. When he was alone and the room was quiet, he thought of the bridge. The plans were as clear as ever in his mind. He knew exactly what had to be done next, what each step of the work would be, what problems had yet to be met and solved.

Then he began to have recurrences of the attack. All the symptoms would return: dizziness, nausea, double vision, cramps, and sometimes unconsciousness. He sensed, without being told, that Doctor Smith was beginning to fear for his life again. Other doctors were called in for consultation; new treatments were tried; but there was no improvement.

One morning after a mild attack, Washington wrote a note to Emily when she came into the room. They had begun communicating by note when it was impossible for him either to speak or listen.

March 1872: The New York caisson partially submerged, approximately eight months after work was begun on the New York end of the bridge.

"Bring the bridge plans, all my calculations and notes from the office. Also ruled paper and pencils. Set up table by my bed."

"Too tiring," Emily wrote. "You can't work now. Wait till you're better."

"I intend to get well," Washington answered, "but some things my assistants have to know now." He paused, struggling desperately to find words that would convince Emily. "Can't lose control of the bridge," he wrote finally. "It's my responsibility. Have to finish it!"

Emily stared at the note for a long time. Then she looked at him. He could imagine how he appeared to her: pale, exhausted from the pain, limp, and helpless. How could she know the strength that still surged deep inside him, the knowledge and skill that he had to use or die?

She left the room and a few minutes later reappeared with her arms loaded with papers and notebooks. She fixed a work table for him beside the bed and devised a wooden tray that he could hold on his lap. He could see the concern and uncertainty on her face. With an enormous gratitude he realized that she understood; she knew that without the bridge his life was worthless, anyway.

At first he could only work for a few minutes at a time, then half an hour, then an hour. When he finished one of these sessions he would sink into a deep sleep, as tired as though he had swung a sledgehammer all day. Slowly, steadily, he wrote out in detail each step of construction that remained.

Martin, Farrington, and his other assistants kept in touch with him through Emily. He learned that the excavation on the New York side had been finished and the caisson filled with concrete. Crews were busy now with the masonry on the tower and with the Brooklyn anchorage.

The Brooklyn anchorage.

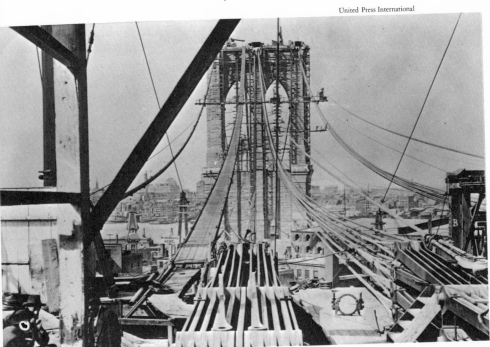

Through the long winter of 1873 Washington used all his strength to complete the instructions for the bridge. He parceled out his energy carefully, conserving it for his working hours. At last, one day in June, he was finished. Everything he knew about the Brooklyn bridge—every measurement and specification, every machine that would be needed, and all the other material and equipment—all this had been recorded carefully. Now, even if he died, the bridge could be completed.

Doctor Smith and Emily lifted him out of bed and into his chair by the window that afternoon. The warm sun bathed his face and arms. Out in the river he could see the unfinished towers rising out of the water, already tall enough to dwarf most of the buildings on either side.

This was one of Washington's "good" days. He could talk with Emily almost normally, and the pain in his legs was hardly noticeable. He was having days like this more frequently now; it seemed to him that there was a chance he would yet recover.

"Spring again," he said, "and here I sit! It's hard to believe that it's been a year since I worked at the bridge."

"I'm just grateful you're alive," said Emily.

"So am I, of course . . . but you know, I am getting stronger all the time. What do you think of taking a trip to Europe this summer, now that I have the plans finished? Doctor Smith said he thought a long cruise might do me good, hurry up the mending process."

Emily looked at him strangely. "I'd like the trip, if you want to go. And I do think it would be good for you to get out of this house, this room. But . . . Washington, don't—well, don't expect too much."

"You don't think I'm going to get well, do you?"

"I don't know. I hope you will. But I want you to be prepared to face the possibility of . . . "

"Of spending the rest of my life like this? No, I'm not

prepared to face it. I'm going to get over this! Wait and see, I'm going to!" His voice broke, and he felt his larynx tightening again. He snatched a piece of paper from the table and scribbled: "I will not be an invalid!"

A week later they sailed for Germany. Washington's younger brother, Charles, went along to push his chair and lift him in and out of bed. Washington spent long hours on a deck chair, baking his injured body in the sun. They went to Weisbaden, a famous health resort, and for several months he followed the prescribed "cure"; a combination of sun, good diet, and warm baths. He had never had much faith in his father's hydropathic medicine, but now he was willing to try anything.

He did seem to notice some improvement, though not as much as he had hoped. And, as Emily had predicted, it did him good to have a change of scene. Now that the bridge was not within sight of his window, he could forget it for hours at a time.

They sailed for home in November, 1873. Washington told himself that he was much better, that his voice was stronger and the pain had eased. He was disappointed that the paralysis was as complete as ever. But perhaps, when the other symptoms were gone . . . .

When the boat docked in New York, it took them several hours to go through customs. By the time a carriage took them home, it was dark and Washington was exhausted. The noise and confusion had grated on his nerves until now even the sound of the horses' hoofs was excruciating. As Charles eased him out of the door and into his wheelchair, he felt a wrenching pain in his abdomen, and once again the world exploded before his eyes.

He woke in the hospital. Looking around at the drab little room, he remembered how he had passed out while being helped out of the carriage. His mind was completely clear. Another attack, of course, a bad one. He knew now that he would never get well.

12 man at the window

Washington sat by the window of his bedroom, a blanket wrapped around his aching legs. He felt a hundred years old. The bridge was growing before his eyes, but now he was only a spectator—and that was all he would ever be. It was out of his hands. He was a helpless cripple, with nothing left but a mind that would not stop functioning even when its ideas could not be carried out.

There was a soft knock on the door, and Emily came in with Charles Martin.

"Colonel Roebling," said the assistant engineer, "I'm sorry to bother you, but we're having some problems on the towers. They've gotten so high that the men on top can't communicate with the ones running the machines below. I wondered if you would have any suggestions. . . . "

"I don't know," said Washington wearily.

"We've had several accidents lately, because of this. I thought possibly we might use flags to signal . . . "

"Whatever you think best. I'm very tired, Charles."

"Oh, I'm sorry, I'll come some other time." Martin left, looking embarrassed and a little hurt.

Emily went out with him, but a few moments later she was back. She stood in the middle of the room and glared at Washington. Obviously something was bothering her, and she

Courtesy CF&I Steel Corporation

"The bridge was growing before his eyes." A later stage of construction viewed from the Brooklyn side.

wanted to talk about it. Couldn't she see how miserable he felt? He sighed and leaned back in the chair, hoping she would go away, but she stood her ground.

"The fearless Colonel Roebling," she said scornfully.

"What?"

"I remember once, when you were telling me how brave everyone thought you were, that I said I wondered how much courage you'd have when you had to face a real tragedy. Now we know."

Washington could not believe that this cruel, unsympathetic woman was his Emily. How could she speak to him that way, knowing how sick he was?

"What do you expect me to do?" he asked in an injured tone. "I can't walk, I can't go anywhere, I can't even talk to anyone for long!"

"I'd like to see you stop thinking about what you can't do!

117

You're thirty-seven years old. Do you plan to spend the next thirty or forty years sitting in that chair and feeling sorry for yourself?"

"Should I take up stamp collecting? Engineering is my life! If I can't do that . . . "

"There you go again, talking about what you *can't* do. Why can't you be an engineer? You have the same knowledge, the same creativity that you had when you could walk!"

"But I can't communicate what I know! I can't inspect what's being done. If something goes wrong, I can't be there to see what it is and correct it. As a matter of fact, Emily, I'm thinking of resigning as Chief Engineer of the Brooklyn Bridge."

Emily studied him for a moment, then sat down beside him. "I have an idea, Wash. I know you're tired, so we don't have to talk about it now, but I want you to think it over. Why couldn't you teach me engineering—just enough so that I could be your representative, could communicate for you? You said that's all you really needed. I could carry your ideas to the bridge, and then I could describe what's happening there to you."

"I've tried working through assistants . . . "

"But this would be different. You haven't been able to keep in touch through Martin and the others because it was too much commotion for you, with them coming in and out all the time. I'm here, anyway. Besides, you need them to supervise the actual work at the bridge. I wouldn't have any other responsibilities, and you could take as much time as you needed to explain things to me."

"But first there'd be so much I'd have to teach you . . . oh, no, it would never work."

"My brother would help with the teaching part. I'm sure he could get away for a week or two."

"It's impossible. Who ever heard of a woman engineer?"

"I'm not suggesting that I go through Rensselaer—just

118

that I learn enough to understand the language and the general plan of this bridge. I can do it. I used to study Gouv's books, on my own, and I was always good at mathematics. Don't dismiss the idea now. Rest awhile, and think about it."

Washington struggled with the suggestion for several days. At one moment he would conclude that it was ridiculous, and then again he would admit that Emily was exceptionally intelligent and might just be able to do it. What finally decided him to try it was the alternative—the final loss of hope and half a lifetime to be frittered away somehow.

G. K. Warren came down from his home in Rhode Island, and together the two men worked with Emily. They tested her knowledge of geometry, which was already quite adequate, and calculus, with which she needed a good deal of help. They taught her how to determine the stress various materials could stand, how to calculate a cantenary curve, how to read and understand bridge specifications. They went through the plans for the Brooklyn Bridge with her step by step and explained the details of cable construction.

Washington could not stay with these study sessions for more than an hour at a time, but Gouverneur and Emily worked all day and into the night.

"I really think she's going to get through this," Washington told Gouverneur one evening after Emily had left the room to fix supper. "She does as well as any engineering student I ever saw."

"When you asked me to come down and help you teach her, I didn't have much faith in the idea," Warren confessed. "I only agreed because your letter made it sound so—so urgent. But now I do believe Emily will be a great help to you. I always knew she was clever, and yet I couldn't take her interest in mathematics and engineering seriously."

"She's quite a woman."

G. K. Warren picked up a newspaper he had been reading

earlier. "I see the legislature is considering making the bridge a public work."

"Yes, Kingsley was here the other day to tell me about it. He said it seems sure to be passed. It will take the bridge out of the hands of private investors, and the two cities will take over—New York's to assume two-thirds of the cost and Brooklyn one-third."

"Do you think it's a good idea?" Warren asked.

"Yes, I suppose so. I'm tired of listening to hints of corruption and fraud. Though I don't think this will stop the critics entirely. Kingsley said he's to be on the new Board of Directors, and most of the others will carry over too. But, at least, with the cities taking the responsibility, we may be able to get the money and materials we need."

When he could not stand any more talk, Washington worked on a model of the bridge while Emily and her brother carried on the studies in another room. Washington constructed the model carefully with pieces of wood, metal, tiny stones, and threads for the cables. Often seven-year-old John would come to his room after school and sit quietly beside him, watching the miniature bridge going together.

The model was a help in teaching Emily, too. Using it, they could show her just how the anchorages would look when completed and how the towers must be finished.

When they were ready to instruct her in the cable spinning, they all sat around the model and Washington attached a thread to one of the anchorages. He looped it over the top of the "Brooklyn tower" and starting moving the spool toward the New York side.

"The reel of wire is in a scow," he told Emily. "As the boat moves across the river, the wire is played out and allowed to sink to the bottom. When it gets to the New York side, it's attached to a hoisting engine, raised to the top, and fastened to the anchorage on the other side. Then you do another wire the same way, and the two ends are spliced together around the driving wheels at the anchorages. That's how you get your traveling rope for the cable spinning."

"What about the river traffic?" Emily asked. "Wouldn't it be dangerous to try to raise a wire from the bottom with all the boats that go by?"

"The engineers will have to wait for a clear spot."

"What happens after they get the traveling rope ready?"

"Someone will have to take the first ride across it, just to show the workmen it's safe and put on a show for the spectators. Farrington, I suppose." Washington was silent for a moment, thinking how it would be: the slow pull up to the top of the first tower, then a pause and the plunge out across the curving rope, the chair swaying between the sky and the shining river.

"How will they start the actual cable spinning?" asked Emily, bringing him back to the present.

"The wire will be mounted on drums at the Brooklyn anchorage," said Washington. He lined up spools of thread on the model to demonstrate. "Then a traveling wheel will be fastened to the rope, the wire will be fed onto it, and it will go back and forth, carrying the wire from one side to the other."

By the time G. K. Warren was ready to go back to Newport, Emily had been taken through the whole bridge plan and the procedures involved in the building process. She could do the basic calculations required and could answer their questions on machines and materials. They had even spent one afternoon looking at samples of wire, which Washington had asked the factory to send, so that she could judge the relative strength and flexibility of different kinds of wire.

"Little sister," said Warren, as he stacked his traveling bags by the door, "you're not a bad engineer—for a woman!"

"You would have to add that." Emily laughed. "And I

thought I had finally cured you of those old-fashioned notions about male superiority."

"What will you be working on when you get back?" Washington asked his brother-in-law.

"We still have to finish the new fortifications in Narragansett Bay."

"Gouv, aren't you ever tempted to resign from the Army?" Washington spoke slowly, saving his voice as he had learned to do. "I know you could earn more money doing civil engineering and work on more important projects, too. After all, the Army hasn't done much for you. . . . "

"I'll never resign; at least not until my name is cleared. If I left with that blot on my record—well, I just won't. I'm Regular Army, Washington; it's been my life, and I'm not going to leave branded as an incompetent."

"Five Forks was a long time ago, Gouv," said Emily.

"To me it was only yesterday."

"How is your appeal coming?" asked Washington.

"I keep writing letters to the War Department, and they keep putting me off. I don't suppose I'll get a hearing while Grant's in office; he was too much involved. But some day I'll get my inquiry."

When Warren left, Washington spent a few more days working with Emily. They hired a young couple to live with them as cook and butler. The man could also lift Washington in and out of bed, and his wife doubled as a nurse for Johnny when Emily had to go out.

A week later Washington called a meeting of the engineering staff. They all came to his sitting room one bright December morning—Charles Martin, Frank Farrington, Francis Collingwood, William Payne, George McNally, Wilhelm Hildebrand, Sam Probasco.

Washington studied their faces before he spoke. They were

respectful, attentive, but perhaps a bit curious, too. He had not seen any of them except Martin and Farrington since his first attack. He knew they must be wondering whether he was still capable of carrying on as Chief Engineer.

He began the meeting by asking for reports on the current state of the bridge. He had saved his strength all through the previous day so that he could make a good appearance at the meeting. Their faces showed increasing confidence in him as he prodded them with questions and made suggestions.

Then it was time for the main business of the meeting. He called Emily into the room and began: "Gentlemen, I think that if I'm to continue as Chief Engineer of the bridge I'll have to keep in closer touch with the work. Since it's impossible for me to visit the site myself, I've decided to use a representative who can keep me in communication with you and with the work: my wife."

He saw the shock and dismay with which they reacted to the idea. Quickly he told them of the intensive training he and Warren had given Emily. Still they looked unconvinced, so he began questioning Emily and invited them to test her knowledge as well. She handled his questions deftly, and soon the assistant engineers joined in:

"How much masonry will go into the New York anchorage?"

"About sixty thousand tons."

"How will the cables be constructed?"

"Each cable will have nineteen strands of 278 Number Eight B.W.G. wires."

"How long will the wires be?"

"A million feet, or almost two hundred miles long."

The interrogation went on for nearly an hour, and to Washington's satisfaction, Emily got through it without a single slip. The engineers were impressed, he could see that. He decided to ask for a vote of confidence before they had a chance to change their minds.

"Well," he said, "what do you think? Can Mrs. Roebling serve as a go-between, keep us in communication?"

The men were silent, and Washington sensed their uneasiness. They glanced at each other, waiting for someone to declare an opinion. Then Charles Martin spoke.

"If you believe it will work, it's certainly worth trying. I think we'd all agree that Mrs. Roebling has an amazing knowledge of the bridge. . . . " The others were nodding and smiling now. Washington felt a rush of gratitude for their loyalty. It had been two years since he had worked with them actively, and yet they were still willing to accept his leadership—even try something completely unorthodox.

He was suddenly tired; his legs ached, and his nerves were raw from the talk. Martin stood up and said hesitantly, "There's something you should know.

"We're nearly out of stone, cement, lumber—and our recent orders haven't been filled. I wrote an urgent note to Mr. Kingsley about it, and today I got this answer." He handed Washington a piece of paper, his note to Kingsley. Across the bottom was scrawled in Kingsley's familiar handwriting:

Orders cannot be filled until further notice. Funds for the bridge are exhausted.

13 profits and politics

Through the dreary winter of 1876 Washington looked out his window at the idle machinery and unfinished towers at the bridge site. If private investors had been an uncertain source of funds for the bridge, the two cities were proving even more unreliable. The newspapers were full of controversy. Some urged the immediate resumption of the work; some suggested it was time to scrap the project completely; some straddled the fence, wanting the bridge to be finished but contending that it was costing too much.

In January Washington had a letter from his brother, Ferdinand:

Dear Wash:

Charles and I are planning to come to New York next week and we need to see you. We think it's time the company was formally organized—it's getting too big for us! Business is excellent; we have more orders for wire than we can possibly fill.

How are you? No doubt the stoppage of work at the bridge is frustrating, but don't let it get you down. When the politicians are done squabbling you can get back to work.

We'll be in on Tuesday afternoon. Let us know if you don't feel up to seeing us then.

Your brother
Ferd

When Charles and Ferd arrived, Washington was sitting in the parlor. He felt stirrings of self-pity as they stamped in out of the cold, their cheeks glowing and their hair sprinkled with clean new snow. Once he had been the active one in the family. He remembered going out sledding when everyone else thought it was too cold and stormy. He almost let himself think that it should have been one of them who became an invalid; they wouldn't have minded so much.

Disgusted with what had been going through his mind, Washington concentrated on his two brothers. As he exchanged greetings with them, he thought what a contrast there was between them. Ferd was the outgoing one; sure of himself, quick to make decisions with instinctive good judgment. Charles looked young in spite of his handlebar moustache. He was quiet, almost shy, and he preferred to work alone.

As long as Charles handled engineering problems for the Roeblings and Ferd stuck to business management, they got along fine, but Washington knew that there had been some clashes when their duties converged. Apparently the only thing all three of them had inherited from John Roebling was stubbornness.

"You look fine, Wash," Charles was saying.

Washington was glad he had asked the butler to carry him out to the parlor. He knew he looked more normal here, away from the sickroom. "What's this about organizing the company?" he asked, and his voice was clear and strong for once.

"It's got to be done," said Ferd. "We should have incorporated long ago. Our family's too big to get along with just an informal agreement and the terms of Father's will to go by. We could get into all kinds of legal trouble. I had our lawyer draw up some papers, and everybody met back in Trenton to talk things over. We just need your approval now."

"I see." Washington struggled against a feeling of use-lessness. Everything had been done without him; all they wanted was his signature on a piece of paper. He glanced at the sheets Ferd handed him and saw the name of the company: "JOHN A. ROEBLING'S SONS."

Then, a little farther down he saw something that completely amazed him. He blinked and read it again: *"Washington Augustus Roebling, President."*

"What's this?" he asked when he could speak. "But surely you don't mean to make me president, with things as they are." He gestured awkwardly at his crippled body.

"You're ideal for it," said Ferd. "We never even considered anyone else! In the first place, you're the eldest, the one who worked most closely with Father. . . . "

"But. . . "

"As for your health, that won't make any difference. We can meet here, when we need to. You're the only one of us who can grasp the whole operation, Wash. You've worked in the factory; you've done designing; and you've actually used our products in building some of the most famous bridges in America. I see things in terms of profit and loss, expansion and publicity. Charles is all wrapped up in the operation of the factory and drawing up plans for our customers. The others don't even know one phase of the business well. It has to be you!"

President of John A. Roebling's Sons! Washington was ashamed of his delight. He knew it was largely an honorary position—with a salary that would give him security even if the Brooklyn Bridge were his last project. But somehow the news restored his self-respect. He was needed; he was important.

The business was soon settled, and the brothers stayed for supper. Talk at the meal centered around their main interest—the company.

"We've put in a galvanizing train next to the old rope

shop," said Charles. "Right now I'm experimenting with methods of putting on a coat of zinc that won't crack when the wire is bent."

"Speaking of wire, when will they be ready to take bids for the Brooklyn Bridge cables?" Ferd asked.

Washington had to take a long drink of water before answering. His voice was beginning to show the strain of the afternoon's talk. "That depends on when we get the work going again! We could be ready to spin cables this spring, if we had the funds. As it is, I'd say it'll be summer before they're ready to receive bids for wire."

"You think we'll get the contract?"

"It's not up to me, of course. The board will give it to the low bidder. But I doubt that any other company can meet the specifications: galvanized steel wire, with a tested strength of a hundred sixty thousand pounds per square inch, no spots and uniform quality—I don't know another firm that can produce it, and I don't think I'm prejudiced."

"Will they want Bessemer or crucible cast steel used?"

"That I don't know. My guess would be Bessemer, because of the lower cost. But you'd better prepare a bid on crucible cast steel wire, too."

When Ferd and Charles left to go to their hotel that night, Washington went to bed immediately. He lay between the crisp, cool sheets, relaxing gratefully. His throat ached, and his legs were stabbed by frequent pains. But he was happier than he had been for months. His mind swirled with plans for the company, the bridge, for other projects in the future. When he closed his eyes he saw again those words on the articles of incorporation: *"Washington Augustus Roebling, President."*

It was May before the construction got under way again. After months of haggling, New York and Brooklyn paid their shares of the cost, and the engineers got their long-awaited shipments of bricks and cement and steel.

On the morning that full working crews were due to report, Emily had breakfast with Washington before setting out for the bridge. He had spent recent days briefing her on how the anchorage should look, details of the work that would be going on now, and problems to watch for. There seemed to be nothing left to say as they shared the hot coffee, biscuits, and applesauce Emily had brought on a tray.

She stood up and began to tie on her bonnet before the mirror. She was wearing a severe, black dress, and the hat she had chosen was just as plain.

"Where's the funeral?" Washington asked.

Emily turned, her white face looking even paler against the clothes. "Oh, do you think it's too. . . ? I just didn't want to look —well—frivolous."

"Darling, you're going to have to show them that you can think like an engineer, but I doubt that any sort of clothes could make you *look* like one!"

"Oh, Wash, I'm so scared!" Emily sank down on the side of the bed, twisting her hands together. "Will they laugh at me or just ignore me or what?"

"You know what it's all about," Washington reassured her. "They'll see that soon enough."

"It's just that I want so much to do this, for you. . . ." Washington put an arm around her shoulders and patted her. She kissed his cheek, sighed, and got up again. A few minutes later Washington watched her walking toward the river—a small, almost pathetic figure in black, her feet dragging like a child on the way to school in the sweet spring weather.

Washington spent the rest of the day watching the work at the Brooklyn anchorage through his field glasses. Emily had taken the ferry to the New York side, where the anchorage was still incomplete. That was the one part of the bridge he could not see well, even with his telescope, because of the buildings between the river and the anchorage.

At six-thirty he heard Emily come in. He propped himself up on a pillow and waited in acute suspense until she opened the bedroom door.

He knew at a glance that she had had a good day. She had taken off the bonnet, and her brown hair framed a flushed and happy face. "It's going so well," she began in a rush of words, "and everyone was so nice. . . oh, I've got a thousand things to tell you!"

Washington listened as she told of the progress made through the day, the courtesy the assistant engineers and workmen had shown her, the questions she had asked. He heard in her voice the same excitement he had always felt the first day on a new project, and he enjoyed it almost as much as though he had been there himself. He could delight in her happiness and share her triumph; it was nearly as good as being able to go to the bridge.

In the days that followed, their partnership developed until Emily could tell instinctively what he would want to know. She was his eyes and ears, and she quickly learned to speak the lanuage of bridge builders.

On a sweltering day in August she stayed home with Washington and watched Frank Farrington take the first ride across the traveling rope from Brooklyn to New York. As he sped across the river in a boatswain's chair, waving a red bandanna, a large crowd cheered and cannons blasted a tribute from the deck of a ship. It was all over in a few minutes.

"Now we should be able to get on with the cables," said Emily, "after the footbridge is up."

"Yes, and I'm still working on a way to speed up the cable

Harper's New Monthly Magazine, May, 1883

Farrington crossing the span.

spinning. I think I can design a machine that will save a lot of time and work."

Emily leafed through one of his scientific journals while Washington studied his plans. Suddenly she exclaimed, "Wash! Listen to this!" She read from the magazine:

CAUSE OF CAISSON DISEASE DISCOVERED

Paul Bert, a well-known French physiologist, has published findings which identify the cause for caisson disease or "bends" which has plagued deep-sea divers and users of pneumatic caissons.

Caisson disease, according to Bert, is caused by the escape of tiny bubbles of nitrogen into the bloodstream during decompression, which interefere with circulation. If the bubbles get into the joints they cause pain in the joints; if they are released into the muscles they cause muscle cramps; if they are carried into the nervous system they produce paralysis; if they enter the heart they cause death.

Bert also maintains that the effects of caisson disease could be minimized or eliminated by slow decompression.

"Bubbles of nitrogen," said Washington thoughtfully. "I suppose it makes sense. And he says that slow decompression is the answer! When I think of how we tried to prevent it with health rules and hot coffee. . . . "

"At least, if this man is right, there'll be no need for more deaths and injuries from the bends."

"Yes," Washington said, "now engineers can use pneumatic caissons without fear; all they have to do is take the men out slowly, by gradual stages. They could have a series of air locks with the pressure a little lower in each one."

"You'd better get some rest now," Emily told him, laying the journal aside. Washington closed his eyes as she left but one thought tormented him for a long time before he fell asleep: Why couldn't the Frenchman have made his discovery six years earlier?

It was time to let the bids for the cable wire. Ferd wrote to Washington that he had submitted a bid of six and three-fourths cents a pound for Bessemer steel wire and nine cents a pound for crucible cast wire. Washington felt sure that the family firm would get the contract. They were, after all, the oldest and largest producers of wire rope in the country. Their products had proven safe in many large bridges, and they had much more experience than any other company.

Then William Kingsley asked to see him. Washington had a feeling that it had something to do with the wire bids, for the contract had not been let. Kingsley came to the house one rainy morning in September, and his overhearty greetings made Washington uneasy. The businessman strolled around the room, smoking cigars and making small talk, until finally he brought up the matter of the wire bids.

"You should know, Colonel Roebling, that there is some talk—well, that you want to see the wire contract go to Roebling's Sons."

"What do you mean? Of course I want to see them get the contract! I can trust the wire, I know how it's made and that it's the best there is."

"But you also happen to be president of the company, and you own a good bit of the stock. . . . "

"What has that to do with it? I don't let the contract; the board will give it to the lowest bidder who can meet the specifications. If some other company can produce quality wire for less money, they'll get the contract."

"Still, you have to think how it looks, with the Chief Engineer of the bridge also president of the company that is the main contender for a big wire order. Frankly, Colonel, it's been suggested that you should resign as president of John Roebling's Sons and sell your stock."

There was silence between them as Washington stared out the window, trying to master his anger. Then he said softly: " 'There's talk,' 'it's been suggested'—come now, who's doing the talking?"

Kingsley looked uncomfortable. "Several members of the board agreed, but—I believe Congressman Hewitt brought it up in the first place."

Hewitt! Abram Hewitt was one of the most powerful men in New York, a member of the House of Representatives, son-in-law of the wealthy Peter Cooper, a philanthropist, lecturer, and scholar. Hewitt was highly respected. A democrat, he had been one of the reformers who helped destroy Boss Tweed. It was this reputation for honesty and courage that had brought his appointment as head of a committee to investigate the finances of the Brooklyn Bridge.

Thus far the Hewitt committee had found no major irregularities in the use of money on the bridge. They had suggested the change to municipal ownership and had done much to quiet the newspapers' criticisms. All this would seem to make Hewitt a man Washington could admire and trust.

Yet. . . what personal contact he had had with Hewitt had left him uncertain. For one thing, the congressman and his father-in-law owned a huge iron and steel plant in Trenton. Although they did not produce wire, they had been rivals of the Roebling company since John Roebling stopped buying iron rods from Cooper and Hewitt and began manufacturing his own iron and steel.

Washington had met Hewitt several times and had found him pompous and superior. He asked himself whether the rivalry and personal dislike made him suspicious now. Perhaps Hewitt was right. . . but no, it was unfair!

"My father used Roebling wire on the Niagara, Cincinnati, and Allegheny bridges, and no one questioned that."

"But that was before any other companies were making wire rope," said Kingsley. "And there have been so many charges of fraud in the building of this bridge; we don't want to invite more."

"What if I refuse to resign and sell my stock?"

"Then I'm afraid the contract will have to go to another company. Mr. Hewitt introduced an amendment at our last meeting stating that no company in which a trustee or engineer has an interest is entitled to make a bid. It was passed."

"All right," said Washington slowly, "I suppose I'll have to do it." His mouth tasted bitter, and he had to exert a supreme effort to control his voice. "I want Roebling wire in my cables

—not so I can make a profit, as you seem to think, but because I have confidence in it."

"Of course, of course," said Kingsley soothingly. "I understand. It's just for the sake of appearances."

"How many other bids do you have?" Washington asked.

"There's only one other firm that could meet the specifications—J. Lloyd Haigh."

"Haigh! I've seen some of his wire; it's lumpy and brittle. Why, the man's known as a scoundrel. I know an engineer who contracted with him and got wire that wouldn't be fit to hold a chicken coop together!"

"You don't need to worry. The Roebling bid for Bessemer steel wire was more than a cent a pound lower than his. And since we've agreed to use the Bessemer type, I think the whole thing can be settled quite simply when the board meets."

The next day Washington sent Ferd his resignation as president of the company and empowered him to sell the stock. Washington tried not to admit how much the ruling bothered him. In his letter and his comments to Emily he treated the whole thing lightly. And, in fact, the loss of income from the stock did not worry him; he could save what he earned from the sale of stock and use its interest to live on, together with his salary as Chief Engineer.

It was having to resign as president that really galled him, and yet he knew it was childish to be so upset about it. The position had restored his self-respect. Now he had lost it through a technicality. Worst of all, his own integrity had been questioned by implication, as though he were some sort of crooked politician. He had never taken a penny that was not rightfully his or used his influence for anything but the good of the bridge!

In December Washington learned that the executive committee of the bridge corporation had unanimously recommended that the contract for Bessemer steel wire be awarded to John A. Roebling's Sons. Now all that remained was for the full board to meet and give formal approval, and the Roebling firm could begin manufacture of the more than three thousand tons of wire that would be needed.

The board was to meet on January 11, 1877. Washington waited impatiently through the day for the notification that the contract had been approved. There had been too many delays already; he wanted to be ready to start the cable spinning at the first hint of spring.

They were just about to eat supper when the expected knock sounded on the front door. But Emily brought Charles Martin to his room instead of Kingsley or a representative of the board. Martin's face was red, and his eyes flashed angrily as he spoke.

"Jim Stranahan, a friend of mine on the board, just told me—they've awarded the wire contract to Haigh!"

14   the spider spins

Washington could not believe what he had just heard. "Haigh? But that's impossible! I know the executive committee recommended the contract be given to Roebling, and Haigh's bid was more than a cent higher!"

"They decided to use crucible cast steel, and he had a slightly lower bid on that."

"But Kingsley told me they had decided to buy the Bessemer!"

"Hewitt wrote a letter to the board, convinced them that crucible cast wire would be more durable. Haigh's bid for that type was three-tenths of a cent lower. Jim Stranahan suggested that they give your brother a chance to make another bid, but that was rejected and the contract was awarded to Haigh."

Washington sank back against his pillows, weak with anger and frustration. "Crucible cast wire might be stronger—if anyone but Haigh made it! I'm sure Ferd could have met his bid if they'd given him a chance."

"I'm sorry to bring such bad news," said Martin, looking as unhappy as though it were his fault. "I'd better go now; Mrs. Roebling is bringing your supper. . . . "

Washington could not eat the juicy roast that Emily had prepared. It could make no financial difference to him now that the contract had gone to Haigh—and for that matter he had never been concerned about the money the contract would bring into the Roebling firm. But the bridge! How could he trust those slender threads on which the whole structure depended? If the wire in the cables was of poor quality, he could never be sure. . . .

"Charles told me about the contract," Emily said as she came to get his untouched tray. "Is there anything we can do about it?"

"Not a thing. The board lets the contracts. What I can't understand is Hewitt. He's obviously planned this, but why?"

"Maybe he has some grudge against you or your family."

"Possibly. But I don't know what it would be. Of course, he may be acting in good faith. But I can't help wondering whether he has some connection with Lloyd Haigh."

"You mean he might be getting some profit from the deal? If that's true, a lot of people are very wrong about Abram Hewitt. He has a reputation for honesty."

"I know," said Washington, "but these days honesty seems awfully rare. Look at the scandals in Grant's administration. And Boss Tweed, right here in New York. That's why people have been so suspicious of the bridge, and of me—they can't believe anyone could be more interested in building something beautiful and lasting than in making money."

"What about the wire? Can we be sure it's all right?"

"We'll have to set up a system of careful inspection. Every inch of that wire is going to be checked before it's sent to the bridge. If Haigh thinks he can sell us poor wire and make his profit that way, I'll make him wish he'd never gotten the contract."

The footbridge was finished in April, and the first wire for the cables was delivered early in May. Washington had designated one of the assistant engineers to go to the Haigh plant in Brooklyn every day and check the wire output. The perfect wire was stamped with approval, and the rest was marked "un-

July 1876: View from New York.

acceptable." The inspector told Washington that a good deal of the wire ended up in the second pile, and he tried not to feel pleased.

The cable spinning began. A traveling wheel, which looked like a bicycle wheel without a tire, moved back and forth across the river, carrying the wire. A cowbell was attached to the wheel to warn workmen when it was coming. As the full wheel went from Brooklyn to New York another empty one made the trip back to Brooklyn. When the wire reached the New York side, it was fastened around the heavy iron "strand shoe" at the New York anchorage.

After a double wire had been run across, it had to be adjusted to the proper sag. Engineers stood on the tops of both towers and signaled with flags until the sag was correct to a fraction of an inch.

Emily spent at least an hour or two every day at the bridge. Washington sat at his window through the long days, watching through field glasses or his telescope, making notes. He directed the work like a spider spinning a complex web—except that he could no longer ride out along the strands to place them according to plan.

When winter came, it was hard to adjust the wires to the proper level. Often snow and ice coated the traveling rope. The workmen were in constant danger on the slippery, swaying footbridge. Several men fell to their deaths that winter, and Washington had to stop the work when the winds were high.

One morning in February Washington heard the butler arguing with someone at the door. Emily was at the bridge, and Johnny at school.

"I tell you Colonel Roebling doesn't give interviews," he heard the butler say. "Certainly not without an appointment."

"It won't take long. Let's see, is this his room?"

The bedroom door opened, and a tall young man entered, followed by the protesting butler. "I'm sorry, he just walked in. . . . "

April 1877: The footbridge and cradles have been built in preparation for the spinning of the cables.

Museum of the City of New York

"All right." Washington knew he had seen the man before, but when?

"It's good of you to see me," said the man, with a triumphant smile at the departing butler.

"I don't seem to have much choice. But I have a feeling this isn't the first time we've met."

"I'm glad to see your illness hasn't injured your memory, in spite of the unfortunate stories one hears. I interviewed you several years ago. . . . "

Then Washington remembered. The insolent reporter who had spoiled his evening at Delmonico's! "What do you want?" he asked coldly.

"My editor wondered if you had heard about the evidence that was given at the Tweed trial yesterday."

"The trial? No, I don't think I read about yesterday's session." The trial of Boss Tweed had been dragging on for months, after a series of delays and a mistrial.

"Kingsley paid Tweed $65,000 to get his approval on the bridge project. They also had a deal that gave Tweed the right to buy stock at an eighty per cent reduction. Naturally, our readers wonder if you knew about the deal. . . . "

"I did not!"

". . . or perhaps had some share in it."

Washington glared at the reporter. If he could only stand up, drive a fist into that sneer, or at least turn his back! Combined with his rage was shock at the news the man had given him. He had always feared something like this, and now that it was out in the open people would surely be convinced that everyone connected with the bridge was dishonest.

"I told you I knew nothing about this," he said finally. The familiar exhaustion that followed violent emotion engulfed him; he wanted only to be rid of the intruder.

"Well, we can print your denial then. And at least I can

say that I saw you. There's a rumor around town that you died six years ago and the bridge officials have hushed it up so they can split your salary between them."

"That's fantastic!"

"Others say you're alive but insane. . . ah, I'm sorry I upset you. I'm really pleased to find that you. . . well, that the rumors are false. Good day!" The reporter left the room with the same maddening self-confidence he had shown at the end of their interview at Delmonico's.

The next day Washington read of their conversation in a story under the heading: "REPORTER INTERVIEWS RECLUSE ENGI-NEER."

" 'Recluse!' " he exclaimed. "Do they think I don't *want* to get out of this room?"

The story was short and correct, as far as it went. The reporter had used the old journalistic trick of spreading rumors by denying them: "Roebling stated that he did not know about Kingsley's bribe of William Tweed, and also that he did not receive any profit from the deal. . . . " "The engineer appeared capable of carrying on a discussion despite rumors that he is mentally incompetent. . . . "

Spring came again, and Washington sat before the window day after day. Since his encounter with the press, he had become conscious of what people were saying and thinking about him. He felt lonely and isolated, not only because he could not go out but because he could not make himself understood. His family and his assistants knew that he had not changed, that only his body had been injured. But those others, those crowds who gaped at the bridge—they would believe what they chose.

His frustration increased one day in June when he watched a serious accident at the bridge. The fifteenth strand of the north cable had just been finished and was being lowered into place.

Washington moved his field glasses up and down the strand as the operation went on, and he noticed that the holding rope was becoming fouled. He wanted to shout to the crew to stop and untangle it.

The holding rope snapped under the pressure. The strand dropped sharply and came loose from the adjusting tackle. Then the end of the strand swept away from the anchorage, carrying with it the cast-iron shoe. The long strand lashed like a whip. The shoe flew over houses and streets, landing finally in the yard under the New York tower. Then the free end whizzed over the top of the tower and the whole strand sank into the river, just missing an excursion boat full of passengers.

Sweat rolled from Washington's forehead; his face ached. He strained to see what was happening, but the far side of the New York tower and anchorage were hidden from his view. What damage had the flying shoe done? Had anyone been hurt? Emily was there somewhere, probably at the anchorage!

Washington looked around at the walls of his bedroom with loathing. Suddenly he could not bear his imprisonment. He grasped the arms of the chair and pushed until he lunged forward, struck his head against the window frame and sprawled on the floor like a rag doll.

The butler found him there, weak and pain-racked but still conscious, and got him into bed. A few minutes later Emily came.

"You're all right?" he asked in a whisper.

"Yes, but what about you? How did you fall?"

"Never mind that. What happened at the bridge?"

"A strand broke loose and carried the shoe with it. Two workmen were struck at the anchorage and killed; three more hurt seriously."

"Oh, no. . ."

"It could have been much worse. The wire just missed a boatful of people." Emily had seemed calm, but now he saw her eyes fill up with tears. She sank down beside him and cried. "Oh, Wash, I wasn't twenty feet away. One minute they were working there, laughing with each other, and then that noise and. . . both men were gone!"

"Do you have any idea why it happened?" Washington asked her. "I saw the holding rope getting tangled, but it doesn't seem as if the whole strand should have broken loose."

"I don't suppose we'll ever know for certain. But there is something I've been meaning to tell you. Some of the wire we've been getting lately doesn't look just right to me. Of course, I don't know too much about it, but I do remember the samples you showed me—and Haigh's wire isn't that uniform. Some of it seems fine, but then again I'll notice a spot or a lump."

"How can that be? Every inch of that wire is being inspected before it's brought to the bridge!"

"I know. . . and maybe I'm wrong. I hope so."

The shoe was replaced the next day, and the wheel was soon traveling across the river as though nothing had happened. Washington remembered how, when his father had died, he had thought of the old legend that "the bridge demands a life." If it was true, then this bridge was demanding many lives.

By midsummer he knew that the cables would soon be ready for squeezing and wrapping. The spinning had gone very well; there was only a little left to be done before they would enter the final stage of the work.

Then one evening Charles Martin came to see him. The heat was stifling, with not even a slight breeze from the river for relief. Washington and Emily were playing a halfhearted game of chess before trying to sleep when they heard the knock on the door.

"Haigh's been sending us defective wire," Martin told them bluntly. "I saw the whole thing tonight."

"What?" Washington asked. "How do you know?"

"Your wife and I both noticed occasional batches of wire that didn't look just right. So the last few nights I've been hanging around the Haigh plant after work, just to see what I could find out. I almost didn't go tonight, it was so hot, but I finally decided to try again.

"I'd been there for almost an hour when I heard the front gate open. I ducked into a doorway across the street to watch. A wagon came out the gate, with two men driving the horses. It was loaded with rings of wire. I followed them, staying out of sight of course, until they came to a warehouse a few blocks away.

"After they drove inside, I found a window I could look through. Inside, they unloaded the wire—I counted eighty rings of it. Then they reloaded the wagon with some rings of wire that were in the warehouse. My guess is, those had already been rejected by the inspector. They just transfer the certificate of inspection to the bad wire and send the good rings in another load. When that wagon comes to the bridge in the morning, I'm going to unwind every ring and check it. Then we'll have positive proof that they've been switching those certificates. All they have to do is have the good wire checked and approved again and send it on to the bridge later."

Washington wiped his face with a handkerchief. "If you're right, how much bad wire has already been put into the cables?"

"I have no idea. For one thing, we don't know how long Haigh's been doing this. I think he started when he found he couldn't keep up with our order because too much of his wire was being rejected—maybe six months ago. That's when he started to fall behind and then suddenly caught up again."

"Six months." Washington's voice was flat. "And how much of the wire in the last six months was defective?"

"Again, we don't know. I'd say close to half."

Late that night Washington lay sleepless in his rumpled bed. Mosquitoes buzzed in and out of his open window, but the air in the room remained motionless and hot.

Six months of bad wire, he thought. . . It would take a year to undo it and spin it again. There had been so many delays already, so much extra expense, and this would be another scandal. But how could he leave things as they were?

And Haigh. What sort of a man would mix brittle, lumpy wire in with the good? And especially for a bridge! Washington had few illusions about himself; he knew his faults and weaknesses. But he had never done deliberately shoddy work. The responsibility to build well—this was the principle on which he had based his life. He could not understand a man to whom it meant nothing.

And now he would have to decide what to do about the weakened cables.

15 too much money

The next morning Charles Martin came back to the house and confirmed their suspicions. He had checked the first wagonload of wire delivered by the Haigh plant and had found in it eighty rings of defective wire. Not only that, but it was Bessemer steel wire, although Haigh had of course charged the higher rate for crucible steel!

Anything Washington did now would be unpleasant. If he insisted the bad wire be removed and replaced, they would lose a year's work and there would be an outcry against the waste of money. If he let it go and relied on the safety margin he had planned, he would never feel quite sure about the strength of the cables. If he tried to take some action against Haigh, many would believe he was taking revenge for the loss of the wire contract.

Washington was still puzzling over the decision when Haigh came to see him that afternoon. The two had never met before, and Washington had formed a mental picture of a big, blustering, villainous sort of man. But Haigh was very ordinary looking, and Washington could see that he was terrified by the prospect of the possible consequences of Martin's discovery.

"I'll admit I sent down some wire that your inspector rejected," he said pleadingly. "But it wasn't so bad. A few lumps or black spots, maybe—I'd still bet that wire would hold up for a hundred years or more!"

"You're betting people's lives!" Washington reminded him. "I'm not willing to do that."

"Most of the wire in the bridge is perfect, even by your standards! And I know you planned the cables to be five times stronger than necessary under the worst possible conditions."

"That's right. I planned a safety margin of five, and I want to have it, with no bad wire whittling it down to four or three. In the future this bridge is going to carry more traffic than we dream of today. I will not have it weakened."

Haigh paced the floor, jerking nervously at his moustache. "Colonel Roebling, my finances are in a bad state. . . . "

"I would have thought that the profits you've made on this contract already would have solved any financial problems you might have. My assistant tells me you've been sending Bessemer steel wire, too, and collecting the crucible steel rate."

Haigh reddened. "Yes, I have sent some Bessemer wire, I admit it. But you must understand. I'm deeply in debt. Mr. Hewitt said he'd foreclose my mortgage. . . . "

"Hewitt?" Washington leaned forward in his chair. "You mean Abram Hewitt has a mortgage on your business?"

"Yes, and I've had to pay him ten per cent of everything I've gotten from the bridge company to keep him from foreclosing."

So that was it! Hewitt was getting a cut of the money Haigh made on the contract! There was nothing illegal about it, of course, just payment on a debt. But Washington seethed, remembering Hewitt's self-righteous pronouncement that no company in which a trustee or engineer had an interest could bid on a contract for the bridge. Haigh was still rambling on about his money troubles, and Washington cut him off impatiently.

148

"Your debts are your own affair, Mr. Haigh, and have nothing to do with the bridge. If we wanted to take you to a court of law, I'm sure we could sue you for every cent you have left."

Haigh was almost quivering, and for a moment Washington thought he was going to get down on his knees. "Oh, please, you wouldn't do that. . . . "

"I don't think so, simply because we haven't the time." Suddenly Washington knew he had made the decision, the only one possible. "I'm going to recommend to the board that you be allowed to retain the contract—provided that you replace the defective wire we haven't used yet, at your own expense, and that the rest of the wire meets our exact specifications. I want you to add enough good wire to make up for the loss of strength we calculate the cables have suffered. From now on we'll inspect your deliveries as they arrive at the bridge."

"Oh." Haigh hesitated. "Well, I'm very grateful that you aren't going to sue. Of course, you'd be within your rights to cancel the rest of the contract. Frankly, it would cost me money to fulfill it by your terms. My plant isn't well enough equipped to produce that much perfect wire; there's so much waste. I had thought perhaps your Roebling works might take over the rest. . . ."

"No! They made a bid; they were rejected. You and Mr. Hewitt were so anxious for this contract—it's up to you to fulfill it. You can't wriggle out just because it isn't as profitable as you thought it would be. Besides, if the contract went to Roebling Sons now, it would look as if I made this whole thing up just to get the order back in the family firm. No, either you supply enough good wire to finish the cables or we'll take it to the courts."

When Haigh had left, Washington wrote a letter to Henry Murphy, the president of the Board of Trustees of the bridge company. Washington explained what had happened and made his recommendation. Then he put the letter in the mail and tried to reconcile himself to it.

At the very worst, there might be two or three hundred tons of faulty wire in the cables. There would be more than three thousand tons of good wire spun when they were finished. The cables were designed so that there would be almost no stress on the individual wires. They would not be twisted but would be bound up straight and wrapped with a protective coating of more wire. All the wire—even the defective rings—had been galvanized, or bathed in molton zinc, to protect it from rusting in the salt spray. Washington knew that with all these safety features a few tons of slightly imperfect wire could not make a great deal of difference.

And yet . . . and yet it rankled him to have to settle for something less than his original specifications, to have to compromise with Haigh's double-dealing. If he had had only himself and the bridge to consider, he would have undone the last six months' work and replaced the wire. But there were the public, the trustees, the officials of the two cities, the critics, and he had to think of them, too. The decision had been made; he would have to put it behind him.

The spinning went on as fast as Haigh could supply wire that met Washington's rigid standards. By October, 1878, the last wire had been run across, and the squeezing began. The wires had already been bound into strands, with 278 wires in each strand. Workmen rode out along the cables and pinched an inner core of seven strands together with clamps. Then twelve more strands were bound around the inner seven, making a hexagonal cable of nineteen strands, almost sixteen inches thick. The four cables were then wrapped with wire. Washington had designed a machine for this job, which moved across the cables and wound a perfect spiral of wire around them.

Harper's New Monthly Magazine, May, 1883

Wrapping the cables.

He and Johnny were looking at rocks one evening in November when Emily came home with bad news. Washington had
become interested in geology during his studies at Rensselaer,
and now it was a hobby he could share with his son. Johnny
had spent the time after school looking for specimens in a nearby
park, and when Emily came into the room, they were trying to
classify them. She gave them a strained smile and pretended
interest in the rocks, but there were worry lines between her eyes.

"What's the matter?" Washington asked her finally.

"Oh, Wash, they're going to stop work again!"

"Money?"

"It's more than that this time. When we were just about
to stop for the day, a couple of lawyers came down to talk to
Charles and me. They claimed to represent something called the
'New York Council for Reform,' and they said they'd filed a

suit to stop the work and forbid any more expenditures on the bridge."

"Reform!" Washington exploded. "That's an interesting idea of reform, to leave a nearly completed bridge standing useless in the river for lack of a few more dollars. What sort of reasons do these so-called 'reformers' give?"

"Oh, we talked with them for half an hour or more, but what they said boiled down to one thing: too much money. They told us their group feels that the bridge company has already spent more than was originally planned and that it might take years to finish it. . . . "

"It certainly will, if they keep on stopping the work!"

". . . but I think there's something else behind this. Oh, they brought in those old stories about the bridge not being safe, too, but I'm sure that isn't the real reason. I have a feeling there are people who don't *want* the bridge finished! Anyway, they said the whole thing will be in the papers tomorrow."

"That should make interesting reading . . . John, where are you going?"

Washington had forgotten that his son was in the room until he noticed the boy opening the door. John turned in the doorway, his expression carefully blank but his dark eyes hurt and angry. "Thought I'd take a walk," he mumbled.

Johnny left the room with the awkward stride of a twelve-year-old. Washington heard him trip over a rug in the hall and then close the front door loudly.

"I shouldn't have told you all that in front of him," said Emily.

"Oh, I suppose he hears things in school. He likes to take his friends to the bridge and show them around, but there are probably others, repeating things they've heard from their parents . . . Well, he'll have to live with it."

The next day the papers were full of the charges made by

the "New York Council for Reform." In addition to the complaints about the amount of money being spent, the "reformers" also claimed that the Brooklyn Bridge would be unsafe. Washington read this part of the story with astonishment:

> *This is wholly an experimental bridge. It is the highest and longest in the world. The history of suspension bridges in this country and in Europe shows their most dangerous exposures to be that to storms, producing oscillations and ruptures . . . . If an eddy of air were to strike the bridge from underneath with greater force than its own weight, it would be lifted, to crash back again with its destructive momentum. . . .*

"An eddy of air strong enough to lift eighteen thousand tons?" Washington slapped the paper down on the table beside his bed. "Whoever prepared this attack can't possibly be that stupid or that uninformed. The investigation by the board of engineers was reported ten years ago, and it fully refuted that sort of nonsense. I think you must be right, Em. There's another reason in back of these charges."

"And I think I've found it," said Emily, holding up another newspaper she had been reading. "Listen to this. One of the New York businessmen behind this says: 'Our city is not a jealous city, but then to ask it to build a bridge in order to send its trade to a neighboring city is asking a good deal even from the best of natures.' And another New Yorker is supposed to have said the bridge is being built 'to drain the resources of the city of New York in order to fertilize the sandy wastes of Long Island.' "

"That may be the answer. The funny thing is, I've heard that the mayor of Brooklyn believes the bridge will move trade out of Brooklyn and into New York. Apparently the men in each city are afraid the other side of the river will benefit more than they will."

As the lawsuit dragged through the courts, the work yards around the bridge were silent again. The partially wrapped cables hung useless between the towers, and children played on the piles of bricks intended for use in the long approaches to the bridge. Christmas was somber that year, in spite of Washington and Emily's attempts to force gaiety for Johnny's sake.

A week after Christmas Washington read another newspaper story which left him limp with horror. The great suspension bridge between Edinburgh and Dundee in Scotland had collapsed with a trainload of people on it!

The Tay Bridge, as it was called, had been opened less than two years earlier. Washington remembered reading about it then and questioning in his own mind the stability of the bridge as it was described. The engineer had not used diagonal stays to keep the roadway rigid, and the wrought-iron braces under the roadway had a strength of only twelve pounds per square foot.

Washington had visited Edinburgh on his first European trip, and now he could almost picture what had happened the previous Sunday afternoon. He saw the storm clouds swirling around the rugged countryside, flashes of lightning slicing through the darkness, and the wind whipping around the bridge. Then the train, the Edinburgh Mail, moved out across the two-mile bridge. A flash of sparks, a crash sounding above the roar of thunder, and then nothing. When two men crawled out along the roadway from the Edinburgh side to see what had happened, they found that a half mile of the bridge, with the train and seventy-five people, had plunged into the river. There were no survivors.

This was the engineer's nightmare, the bridge builder's greatest fear. Washington imagined the same thing happening on the Brooklyn Bridge—and yet he knew that it could not. Storms had never damaged his father's bridges, and this one was

154

stronger than any of the others. But the Tay Bridge disaster would not increase people's faith in the Brooklyn Bridge.

A profound depression settled on Washington Roebling. His cramps grew worse, his voice weaker. He slept long hours in the daytime and then could not sleep at night. He was irritable with his family but resented it when they left him alone to brood.

It was six months before the lawsuit was finally thrown out of court. Even then the charges did not stop. Another committee was organized in May to investigate rumors that the engineers of the Brooklyn Bridge were helping themselves to the funds designated for the bridge. The committee soon reported that the charge was ridiculous, and its conclusion was printed beneath small headlines in the back pages of the newspapers.

When the work finally began again that spring, Washington's spirits revived. He was back at his window, Emily was bustling back and forth with his instructions, and miraculously his pain lessened. He felt sure that the worst was over. There was only the roadway to put up now, and the bridge was so nearly finished that the critics would surely find something else to talk about.

Late one afternoon Washington heard a commotion in the front hall—Johnny's voice and another boy's, raised in argument. He clearly heard the strange voice say:

"I want to see the wizard!"

Then there were thumps, bangs, the sound of running feet, and the bedroom door slammed open.

16 who is washington roebling?

A slender blond boy of about Johnny's age stood panting in the doorway, his shirt ripped and a bruise on his cheek. Johnny was behind him, holding him by one arm. Both froze when they saw Washington propped up in bed facing the door. The strange boy looked terrified.

"What's this all about?" Washington asked.

"He—he just came busting in here," Johnny stammered.

"What do you want?" Washington asked the other boy.

The intruder was so pale that his freckles stood out like mud splatters. "It was a dare," he said finally in a small voice.

"Someone dared you to come here and see me? Why?

"They . . . they call you the 'mad wizard.' And they say you can do magic, and you never let anybody see you. . . . "

"I told 'em it was all just stupid lies," Johnny said furiously. "My friends know better, but I guess everybody else *wants* to believe that silly stuff."

"Come here, you," said Washington. The blond boy moved reluctantly across the room and stood by the bed.

"I am just an ordinary man who is sick, too sick to get out of bed. I can't use my legs; they're paralyzed. I do direct the building of the bridge from here, but not by magic. My wife and other assistants take my orders to the men who are working, and I watch from the window. You understand?"

The boy nodded.

"You think I'm insane?"

"No, sir, and I'll tell my friends you're not. I'm sorry." He ran out of the room and the house.

"John," said Washington when the other boy had gone, "why didn't you tell me about these rumors?"

"Well, I just figured you and Mother had enough to worry about. It wasn't important."

"Maybe not, but it must have made your life pretty unpleasant. I wish I could parade through the streets and convince everyone I'm not a 'mad wizard.' "

"It's all right. We know better."

Washington saw a sort of relief in his son's face, and he realized that John's secret had been a heavy burden for a youngster. How long had he been taunted at school by the ignorant suspicions of his classmates and their parents? Yet he had refused to bring the problem home; this had been his contribution to the family and to the bridge. Remembering the selfishness of his own attitude toward his father's work, his sullen moods and resentfulness, Washington was doubly proud of John Roebling's grandson and namesake.

The workmen were now putting up the suspenders which would hold the floor of the bridge. The original plans had called for wrought-iron suspenders, but Washington had decided to use steel instead. The Brooklyn Bridge would be the first all-steel suspension bridge in the world. He was convinced that this was the metal of the future: light, strong, useful in a thousand shapes. Crews brought the steel rope suspenders out on the footbridge and attached them to the cables at exact intervals, which Washington had calculated to the smallest fraction.

For several months the criticism of the bridge stopped, as the nation was shocked by the shooting of President Garfield and his death in September. Then, when the excitement generated by the assassination had cooled, the attacks began again. The *New York Times* asserted that the expense added by the increased use of steel was not only unnecessary but suspicious. Either the original plans had been inadequate or someone was profiting enormously; it was a case of "blunder or plunder." Other papers pounded equally hard on the theme that the bridge was costing too much.

In December James Stranahan made an appointment with Washington. The afternoon of his visit was cold but clear, and the skeleton of the bridge stood out against the blue brilliance of the sky. Washington looked at it through the window as he waited and tried to remember all he knew about James Samuel Thomas Stranahan.

A former railroad contractor, Stranahan was one of the best known civic leaders in Brooklyn. He was reputed to be extremely wealthy. Washington knew that one of his investments was in the East River ferries, and this had made him uneasy when Stranahan was put on the Board of Trustees of the bridge. Yet it was Stranahan who had warned Charles Martin about the Board's action in giving the wire contract to Haigh. Washington could not guess the purpose of today's visit.

James Stranahan arrived promptly, and Washington was impressed with him at once. He was erect and vigorous for a man in his seventies. Something about him seemed to radiate honesty, vision. Having introduced himself, Stranahan went straight to the point.

"You should know what's going on at the Trustees' meetings, Colonel Roebling. I'm here to tell you that and also to ask you some questions."

"More problems, I suppose," said Washington.

"I'm afraid so. Robert Roosevelt introduced a resolution at our last meeting. . . . Well, here, I've a copy of it." He took a piece of paper from his pocket and read:

"Resolved, that the Chief Engineer is requested to report to the Board of Trustees on the total weight that the cables and the suspended structure will be able to bear, and what will be the weight of the suspended structure when completed. . . . "

"Of course I can report on that," said Washington impatiently. "But why the formal resolution? Couldn't they just have asked me for the figures?"

"There's some feeling that you should commit yourself, formally, so there can be no mistake. . . "

"You mean a statement to protect them later, if the bridge collapses?"

"Something like that. Now, could you summarize the facts for me? Just how will the change to steel affect the strength of the bridge?"

Washington spent nearly an hour going over the plans with Stranahan. Finally the contractor said, "I'm convinced. This bridge of yours is designed for tomorrow; that's what so many people don't understand. They're all wrapped up in small town jealousies or miserliness. Before many years have passed, New York and Brooklyn will be parts of a great metropolis, hardly distinguishable from each other. Your bridge will carry traffic we don't even dream of now."

"Mr. Stranahan, if you could convince the Board of that . . ."

"I'll try. And I'll do more than that. I plan to back up your request for more steel with my own responsibility and if necessary my own money. On that basis I feel quite sure you'll get your steel."

Washington was stunned. After all the pettiness and double-dealing that had gone on, Stranahan's generosity seemed almost unbelievable. He was still struggling for proper words of thanks when the older man went on.

"One more thing you should know. The opposition to you goes deeper than just doubts about the plans. It has to do with your health and—well, your mental condition. I don't know how to put this tactfully. Very few people have seen you since your accident, and there are rumors that it may have affected your mind. Some people even confuse you with your father and believe that you died in 1869."

"I've heard some of this, but surely the Board members . . . "

"Oh, they know you're not dead. But you are something of a mystery. At a meeting the other day when your name was mentioned, someone said, 'Who is Washington Roebling?' And he was half serious."

"But what can I do about it?"

"It would help a great deal if you could attend a meeting or two. Let them see that your mind is as sharp as ever."

Washington rubbed his eyes, which were starting to ache from the strain of the long conversation. "I couldn't. My attack didn't just leave me paralyzed; it did something to my nerves. I can't talk to more than one or two people at a time, and even then I sometimes have to cut it short. It's hard to explain, but even the idea of sitting in a roomful of people and listening to a meeting makes me shudder. Don't you see, if I tried it I would only convince them that I am insane or mentally incompetent."

"Of course, I understand. I wasn't aware . . . . And you're probably tired from this long afternoon, forgive me. I'll be going now. It's been a privilege to meet you."

A few days later Washington watched Emily and eleven of the trustees walk across the plank footpath which had just been attached to the suspenders—the first official crossing of the bridge. He listened to the cheering crowds, the tooting boat whistles, and was glad Emily could have her moment of recog-

October 1878: City officials and bridge engineers on a tour of inspection.

nition. She deserved it, with all the work she had done—studying engineering, going back and forth to the bridge, trying to take care of her home and family at the same time.

A letter arrived from G. K. Warren's wife, saying he was very ill. Warren had finally been given a hearing, fifteen years after his dismissal at Five Forks. A military inquiry had been started in December of 1879 and had already dragged on for two years. The long struggle was wearing Gouv down, his wife wrote, and she wondered if he would live to see the end.

Doctor Smith had suggested that Washington might make a trip to the country, get away from the room which had been his prison for so long and from the noise of the city. So Washington and Emily decided to go to Rhode Island in June, to give Washington a change of scene and to visit G. K. Warren.

The bridge approaches were nearly finished now, and the

rest of the work would be quite routine. Washington secretly hoped that a rest in the country might even improve his health enough so that he could attend the opening ceremonies when the bridge was finished.

A few days before they left for Newport, a message came from the Board of Trustees. They requested him to attend the June meeting of the Board. He put the note in his pocket.

Several weeks later he received another message, this time a resolution asking him to be present at the next meeting. He wrote a letter in reply.

> *I am not well enough to attend the meetings of the Board, as I can talk for only a few moments at a time, and cannot listen to conversation if it is continued very long. My physicians hope that living out of doors and away from the noise of the city may lessen the irritation of the nerves in my face and head. I did not telegraph you before the last meeting that I was sick and could not come, because everyone knows I am sick, and they must be as tired as I am of hearing my health discussed in the newspapers.*
>
> *There is not a day that I do not do some sort of work for the bridge. . . . I shall be most highly honored to be present at meetings of the Board as soon as I am well enough to be of any use there.*

It sounds arrogant, he thought, reading it over. I never did learn to be tactful. But he mailed it, anyway. It rankled him to have them summon him like a schoolboy. The newspapers soon reported his "insolence" in refusing to attend the meetings, and one quoted the New York City Comptroller as denouncing him and demanding his removal. He wrote another letter, harsher this time, and sent it to the Comptroller:

> *I do not propose to dance attendance on the Trustees. I never did when I was well and I can only do my work by maintaining*

my independence. Various reporters, trustees and curiosity seekers have visited me and found me a live man, and not the driveling idiot they had expected. . . . To build the bridge is quite enough for any man, but to carry the many Trustees on my back too is rather more than I can stand.

Washington's summer was marred not only by the attacks on him in the press but also by the decline of G. K. Warren. Washington had himself taken to Warren's bedside several times, and the two men tried to talk cheerfully, but the ghost of what they had been in the youthful Civil War days haunted them. Then Gouv became too sick for even those short visits. Finally, on August 8, 1882, he died. The court of inquiry still had not announced its decision.

After the funeral, Washington and Emily had no heart to stay in Newport. By mid-August they were back in New York.

And then one evening shortly after they returned, Charles Martin appeared at the door. His usually open, cheerful face was a troubled mask when he came to Washington's bedside. They exchanged greetings uneasily, and Washington's questions about the progress of the bridge were answered briefly. There was an uncomfortable pause, and then Martin drew a paper from his coat and handed it to Washington.

"Jim Stranahan gave me a copy of this resolution that was proposed at the Board of Trustees meeting today," he said. "I . . . I wanted to be the first one to show it to you, so you'd know I didn't . . . Well, it's disgusting."

Washington read the resolution:

> *Whereas the Chief Engineer of the bridge has been for many years and still is an invalid; . . . Resolved, that this board does hereby appoint Mr. Roebling Consulting Engineer, and Mr. C. C. Martin, the present First Assistant Engineer, to be the Chief Engineer of the New York and Brooklyn Bridge. . . .*

17 brooklyn has her bridge

There was a moment of silence, with Martin shuffling his feet uncomfortably. Finally Washington asked: "Did you say this was passed?"

"No, it was tabled until the September meeting. Mr. Stranahan told me he spoke very strongly against it, and others did, too. I hope you understand that I knew nothing about the proposal, and I wouldn't take the position if they did offer it to me. I'll build my own bridges some day, but this one is yours."

"Thank you—but maybe they're right." Washington was suddenly very tired. "My father always believed that an engineer had to be in constant touch with his bridge, feel it growing under his hands and feet. I can't do that."

"Nevertheless, you *have* built this bridge. I haven't done it or Farrington or anyone else." Charles Martin spoke urgently, and Washington knew he was sincere. "We only followed the plans you gave us. What does it matter if you had to communicate on paper and through your wife, instead of with your own voice? Every detail came out of your mind. Anyway, the bridge will be finished in nine months! If your health was a problem, they should have removed you ten years ago."

"That's true. Why now? The work that remains is simple enough. I suppose it's the rising cost of the bridge and the pressure from the newspapers."

"But it's so unfair!" Martin exploded. "If they could only talk to you; if you could explain the reasons for the added expenses . . . "

Washington shook his head. "That's just the trouble. I know this business came to a head because I didn't attend the Board meetings when they asked me to. But I simply can't function in a group of people; certainly not when I'd have to defend my work, probably for hours. There's nothing to be done about it. If they want to remove me as Chief Engineer, they will."

When Martin had left, Washington told Emily what had happened. She refused to share his mood of resignation.

"They can't do it!" she said fiercely. "We have to fight this. They don't understand, that's all. We have to convince them."

"How?"

Emily thought for a moment, then stood up, her eyes flashing. "I know! We'll get support from other engineers! Remember when the plans first were published, how your father got that committee of consulting engineers appointed to go over the plans? When their report was favorable, a lot of critics were hushed up, at least for a while. Why don't you appeal to the American Society of Civil Engineers?"

"I suppose I could write them a letter, explain my position and ask for their support."

"Of course. If they backed you up, it would be pretty convincing. . . . "

"But will they? I haven't been to a meeting of the Society for ten years. Maybe some of them think I've lost my mind. Maybe they'll feel that I can't do my job without working at the site. I don't know how effective a letter would be."

Emily frowned. "That's true. If only you could go to them, answer their questions. . . . Well, write the letter, anyway. We have to do *something*."

Washington struggled with the letter for several days. He

explained the reasons why the cost of the bridge had soared so far above his father's original estimate: the cost of the added steel, the rising prices in the dozen years of construction, the problems with fire and blowouts in the caissons, the wider roadway to accomodate trains with Pullman cars—which had not even been invented when John Roebling drew his first plans!

He also pointed out that he had not been idle since the accident had paralyzed him. He listed the features he had contributed to the bridge and the mechanical improvements he had designed: the machinery for raising stone to the high towers, the footpath which had been used for cable spinning, the method and implements for the spinning.

Finally, he explained how he had kept in touch with the engineers at the bridge through Emily, and he reminded them that there remained only a few months of routine work to be done.

When the letter had been written and rewritten, he showed it to Emily.

"This is perfect," she said. "I don't see how they could help but be convinced."

"I don't know. Just sending a letter can't possibly answer all their questions. The information is there, but I'm afraid it won't have much impact."

"There's something I haven't told you," said Emily. Her expression reminded him of the way she had looked when she had told him she wanted to study engineering, both fearful and determined. "I asked the Society for permission to read your letter and answer their questions. This morning I got a note inviting me to attend their meeting next week."

Washington was angry, and yet he could not help being grateful, too. "You did that without telling me?"

"I was afraid you wouldn't let me do it; you seemed so

depressed, so ready to give up. Please, Wash, I know the bridge, and I know your part in it. I'll read your letter, and then I can explain anything that doesn't seem clear."

"But a woman speaking to the Society of Civil Engineers? I'm amazed they gave you permission to come!"

"I'm sure it was out of respect to you."

"Since they've already invited you, I can't very well object. All right, Em, you give it your best."

The afternoon Emily went to the engineers' meeting at the American Institute Fair Building, Washington read and reread the copy he had kept of his letter. If he had been able to walk, he would have been pacing the floor. How was Emily being received? This was the first time a woman had ever spoken before the Society. Would they be offended by her presence? Could she defend him convincingly?

Emily did not come home alone. With her was the president of the Society! He came to Washington's bedside, smiling broadly, and they shook hands.

"I'm very happy to tell you that the American Society of Civil Engineers voted to support you in your dispute with the trustees of the Brooklyn Bridge. We're sending them a resolution opposing your ouster as Chief Engineer and commending your work on the bridge."

"Thank you," said Washington dazedly, "I don't know what to say. . . . "

"Better thank your wife." The engineer winked. "She did a superb job of presenting your views and explaining your work. And, of course, the fact that she's young and pretty didn't hurt your cause. We also decided that we've had that silly ban on women at our meetings long enough!"

The Board of Trustees voted down the resolution to make Martin Chief Engineer, and Washington was sure that the letter from the American Society of Civil Engineers was a deciding factor.

The bridge was beginning to look finished by the time Washington's position had been reaffirmed at the September meeting of the Board. Electric lights were installed on the roadway—another feature that had not been dreamed of when John Roebling had drawn the first plans. Washington thought of the difference electric lights could have made in the caisson work; how they could have eliminated the fumes and smoke and the danger of fire.

In November, 1882, the military court of inquiry which had been reviewing G. K. Warren's dismissal at Five Forks made its report. The court exonerated Warren and denied every one of Sheridan's accusations!

"Wonderful," said Washington sourly when he read the report in the paper. "Isn't it too bad that they couldn't have done this in 1865. Or even four months ago. It can't make any difference to Gouv now."

"Oh, I don't know," Emily said. "I'm just happy for Gouv that his record was finally cleared. That's what was important to him—to be remembered as a good soldier. He will be now."

After Christmas, plans were begun for the opening ceremonies to be held at the bridge that spring. It was announced that the main speaker would be Abram Hewitt and that William Kingsley would present the bridge to the mayors of New York and Brooklyn. With that news Washington began to feel that the bridge was no longer his. He could have no part in the formal opening, though an invitation had been sent to him out of courtesy. The crowds, the noise, the long speeches, and the confusion would be more than his raw nerves could bear, even for a few minutes.

He imagined Kingsley, who had probably been behind the bribe to Boss Tweed, presenting the bridge to Seth Low, the mayor of Brooklyn, who had been one of the prime movers in the effort to oust Washington as Chief Engineer. He could almost hear the flowery phrases with which Abram Hewitt would celebrate the bridge he had almost destroyed with his manipulations of the wire contract.

Washington got a letter from Hewitt soon after the speakers had been chosen. The Congressman was preparing his oration, and he wanted help! He asked Washington for "comparative examples of great engineering works, which would show that by scientific appliances the cost of the bridge is very much below what would have been possible in any preceding age."

What gall! Washington thought, to expect *me* to help him with his speech—the old windbag!

He replied sarcastically that the Egyptians had built the pyramids by packing pounds of rice into the stomachs of their slaves, while the builders of the Brooklyn Bridge packed tons of coal into steam boilers to do the same thing. He concluded his letter:

> *It took Cheops twenty years to build his pyramid, but if he had had a lot of Trustees, contractors and newspaper reporters to worry him, he might not have finished by this time! The advantages of modern engineering are in many ways overbalanced by the disadvantages of modern civilization.*

It was May 24, 1883, a sun-washed spring day. When Washington was carried to his window after breakfast, the banners were already waving and the streets were crowded with people. The scene was dominated by the Brooklyn Bridge, finished at last after fourteen years.

Washington wanted Emily to attend the ceremony, but she refused. "I'm going to watch everything here, with you," she said firmly.

Five ships from the North Atlantic Squadron were anchored

below the bridge. Like the towers, they were bright with flags and banners. Bands played through the morning, and fire boats chugged up and down the river.

Then the main procession approached the New York tower. New York's famous Seventh Regiment marched out across the span and lined up on either side of the footpath in the middle of the roadway. Then a carriage stopped at the New York entrance. Through his field glasses, Washington could just make out the figures of President Chester Arthur and Governor Grover Cleveland.

The President and his party walked across the bridge between the rows of uniformed troops. Washington winced at the noise: the cannons at Castle William on Governors Island were fired, and also the artillery at the Brooklyn Navy Yard and the guns at Fort Greene. Bells clanged, the crowds cheered, and the boats shrieked their steam sirens and horns. When the din quieted a little, they could hear the silvery chimes of Trinity Church.

Later in the afternoon President Arthur and his party called to pay their respects. They crowded into Washington's sitting room, perspiring in their heavy frock coats, and congratulated him rather awkwardly on the completion of the bridge. It was obvious that they had been warned about his condition and were not sure how to behave toward him.

"We, ah, we only regret that you could not take your rightful place on the platform during the ceremony, Colonel Roebling," said Abram Hewitt.

"Yes, and my greatest disappointment was in not being able to hear your speech." Hewitt flushed, and Washington added, "I'm sure you enlightened everyone as to the true meaning of the bridge."

Opening ceremonies of the New York and Brooklyn Bridge, May 24, 1883.

Courtesy CF&I Steel Corporation

L TO FIRE THE PRESIDENTIAL SALUTE.   MAYOR LOW RECEIVING THE PRESIDENT.

Harper's Weekly Magazine, May 26, 1883

"He did indeed," said Kingsley hurriedly. " 'An emblem of progress,' that's what he called it."

Then the President stepped forward, and all other conversation ceased. Washington forgot his regrets and frustrations.

"I saw a sign in a shop window this morning," said Arthur softly, grasping Washington's hand. "It was just a crude, homemade thing, but I think it summed up the truth about this day.

"And Brooklyn has her bridge." An engraving by Charles Graham from original sketches and from photographs by Gubelman.

'Egypt had her pyramids,' it said, 'and Brooklyn has her bridge.' It's thanks to you, Colonel Roebling, that Brooklyn has her bridge."

Washington napped fitfully after they left. He was exhausted by the excitement and the visitors. He remembered the whole day with a feeling of unreality. Could this be the culmination of all his struggles? What sort of triumph was it, to sit on the sidelines, while the rest of the city celebrated?

Late that evening he and Emily again took their post by the window. The bridge was to be opened to the public at midnight, after a display of fireworks.

The stars were dimmed by the bonfires, Chinese lanterns, and torches on either side of the river. At eight o'clock fifty giant rockets were released, and they exploded above the bridge in a shower of gold, red, blue, and green. The show went on as bands played again. Men on top of the towers touched off geysers of light; parachutes floated down with colored fireballs suspended from them. Finally five hundred rockets were fired at once. And then the electric lights flashed on, illuminating the bridge from shore to shore.

"Was it worth it?" Washington asked the question more of himself than of Emily. "Fourteen years, twenty lives lost—including my own father—and fifteen million dollars. And here I am, nearly useless because of it. I know I'll never build another bridge. Was this one worth all that?"

"What do you think?" asked Emily.

"I don't know. . . . I don't know."

Thousands of people jammed the approaches to the bridge, waiting for the signal to cross. They had paid a one cent toll and were now standing patiently in line for the honor of being among the first to walk the long span.

At midnight the gates were opened. There was a small cheer, but then the river seemed almost silent after the clamor of the long day. The people walked across slowly. Washington thought they seemed awed by the size and majesty of the bridge. He could see some of their faces as they gazed up at the towers with wonder. There were children, old people, lovers. He saw them all and millions more, who would cross in the years to come.

"It was worth it, of course it was," he said quietly.

174

sources

BOOKS

Catton, Bruce, *Glory Road*. Garden City, New York, Doubleday, 1952.

Catton, Bruce, *A Stillness At Appomattox*. Garden City, New York, Doubleday, 1953.

Conant, W. C., *A History of the Bridge*. New York, Harper & Brothers, 1883.

Dictionary of American Biography, Volume XVI. New York, Scribners, 1935, pp. 86–93.

Gies, Joseph, *Bridges And Men*. Garden City, New York, Doubleday, 1963.

Kirby, Withington, Darling, and Kilgour, *Engineering In History*. New York, McGraw-Hill, 1956.

Mumford, J. K., *Outspinning the Spider: The Story of Wire and Wire Rope*. New York, Robert L. Stillson Co., 1921.

Schuyler, Hamilton, *The Roeblings: A Century of Engineers, Bridge-Builders, and Industrialists*. Princeton University Press, 1931.

Smith, H. Shirley, *The World's Great Bridges*. New York, Harper & Brothers, 1953.

Steinman, David B., *The Builders of the Bridge*. New York, Harcourt, Brace & Company, 1945.

Stuart, C. B., *Lives and Works of Great Engineers of America*. New York, D. Van Nostrand, 1871.

Taylor, Emerson G., *Gouverneur Kemble Warren, The Life and Letters Of An American Soldier*. New York, Houghton Mifflin Company, 1932.

Trachtenberg, Alan, *Brooklyn Bridge: Fact and Symbol*. New York, Oxford University Press, 1965.

PERIODICALS

Browin, Frances Williams, "When They Built the Big Bridge." *American Heritage,* October, 1956.

——— "A Builder of New York and His Bridge." *New York Times Magazine,* December 29, 1929.

——— "The Brooklyn Bridge." *Harper's New Monthly Magazine,* May, 1883.

index